P9-EDR-449

This Happy Rural Seat

". . . and if one were to look upon life all round, and see how in all things the extraordinary, the great, the beautiful stand supreme, he will at once know for what ends we have been born."

—*A Treatise Concerning Sublimity*, XXXV

". . . our erected wit, maketh us know what perfection is, and yet our infected will, keepeth us from reaching unto it."

—SIR PHILIP SIDNEY, *An Apologie for Poetrie*

"The majority of people live below the level of belief or doubt. It takes application, and a kind of genius, to believe anything, and to believe anything *. . . will probably become more and more difficult as time goes on."*

—T. S. ELIOT, "*A Note on Poetry and Belief*"

GEORGE LANNING

THIS HAPPY RURAL SEAT

THE WORLD PUBLISHING COMPANY

CLEVELAND AND NEW YORK

Library of Congress Catalog Card Number: 52-5160

FIRST EDITION

HC 253

Manufactured in the United States of America.

For my father and mother

GEORGE WILLIAM and HELEN LANNING

with love

—And also, of course, with a loving aside for Mr. Skeffington, who let me read these pages aloud to him, and barked his approval whenever we came to the word "walk."

CONTENTS

How the Outsider saw it

Beneath him with new wonder now he views
To all delight of human sense expos'd
In narrow room Natures whole wealth, yea more,
A Heaven on Earth: for blissful Paradise
Of God the Garden was, by him in the East
Of *Eden* planted; *Eden* stretchd her Line
From *Auran* Eastward to the Royal Towrs
Of Great *Seleucia*, built by *Grecian* Kings,
Or where the Sons of *Eden* long before
Dwelt in *Telassar:* in this pleasant soile
His farr more pleasant Garden God ordaind. . . .

(IV, 205–215)

Thus was this place,
A happy rural seat of various views. . . .

(IV, 247–248)

And Their last view

In either hand the hastning Angel caught
Our lingring Parents, and to th' Eastern Gate
Led them direct, and down the Cliff as fast
To the subjected Plaine; then disappeer'd.
They looking back, all th' Eastern side beheld
Of Paradise, so late thir happie seat,
Wav'd over by that flaming Brand, the Gate
With dreadful Faces throng'd and fierie Armes:
Som natural tears they drop'd, but wip'd them soon;
The World was all before them, where to choose
Thir place of rest, and Providence thir guide:
They hand in hand with wandring steps and slow,
Through *Eden* took thir solitarie way.

(XII, 637–649)–*Paradise Lost*

And Mrs. Mentone said

"What will become of us?"

PART ONE

Significant Detail

· 1 ·

"IT'S AN old house," Blanche Loyd said, "but this one—" once more she touched with her finger the dusty glass over the photograph that hung on the wall "—this other one," she amended, "is so old that I don't think the adjective—" She broke off, uncertain, and together they continued to look at the long frame house on its bare ridge of ground, with the stand of trees far away behind it. "One wants a *noun*," she said with a smile; and added, absently, "It was built in the seventeen-eighties." She appeared to rummage through her store of nouns. "It's what you might call an institution," she said at length, and looked at him, he thought, apologetically, as if she feared he might find the word formidable and not sufficient to convey whatever the qualities were that she believed an institution ought delightfully to possess, and which, to her thinking, this one did positively gather into itself; into its—as they seemed—unpainted board sides, through its microscopically paned windows and the three doors in the front with—again, as it seemed to him—their preposterously low-placed lintels.

"The rural seat," he, Mr. Komar, murmured, repeating the phrase Miss Loyd had used a few minutes earlier when, during an uncomfortable drop in their talk, he had looked up from his chair and asked what house was photographed there above her filing cabinet, a house quite other and different from the one he had come to see her about.

"It belongs to my cousin now," Blanche Loyd continued, sitting down and, it seemed, relinquishing her attempt to define the rural seat satisfactorily. "It hasn't passed out of the family. I think, so long as there are any of us, it won't."

"I went to Canada a few years ago," said Mr. Komar. "One of those day excursions to Port Stanley."

"That awful town!" She took him up at once, perhaps fearing that he would miss the true flavor of the place, as she had feared he would not recognize the flavor of the house that was, for the family, not so much "old" as, or so she had implied, the very body and unique aura of the Loyds. "It has all the worst features of the vacation towns on this side of the lake, hasn't it?—dirty people, dirty pavilions; so much furtive rush and noise. But," she hastened on, "the country begins not far above it. The family home"—she indicated the photograph—"is not many miles inland from the Port. Until my mother grew helpless, we used to go there every summer. Now," she shrugged, "of course we stay here in Grant Street, and our relatives come to us."

Another silence expanded between them, but this brief confidence of hers, this small relation of her life, which drew in some considerable portion of her family's life, had done something which made a sustained talk no longer obligatory; the silence stretched elastic, comfortably taut, capable of any desired expansion or contraction. He congratulated himself that they were, as he put it, getting along together. The vast impersonality of his own life was of his making, not conscious, perhaps, but certainly not undesired: he took his human involvements chiefly in bits and snatches—a conversation with the waitress at the restaurant where he ate his dinner, a concern for the eccentricities of his old sedan, which he shared with the garageman who had been repairing it for years, an evening of Hearts with his landlady, Mrs. Hlavaty. He was aware of the larger possibilities of life, the beautiful, excruciating entanglements that other people got into, and survived, but these required an enormous effort, and in his observation were rarely worth it; he liked better the passing warmth that asked nothing of him beyond the moment's courtesy or interest. Now, Miss Loyd had placed herself in the same relation to him that the restaurant waitress was in, whose divorced husband's awful conduct in Troy, New York, he knew about, and the garageman, whose wife had what is called a malignant growth. He wondered what she was thinking while she sat there before him, ruffling absently a sheaf of freshly-typed correspondence: he could see the letterhead, "B. Loyd, General Insurance, 728 Bruce Building."

He looked consideringly around room 728 of the Bruce Building. It was a pleasant office, he thought, not small but too small to suggest any considerable affluence or even business aplomb: in fact, the office of a lady—and it was not, in the world that Mr. Komar deliberately inhabited, to be expected that a *lady* should possess either commercial aplomb or too solid finances. He had a reverence for ladies that he knew was anachronistic in this fourth decade of the twentieth century. Innumerable new brooms had for thirty years now been briskly sweeping clean, but in the corners the dust and fuzz still collected. He understood that ladies were part of this dust and fuzz, but he had not wanted to venture out onto the middle of that shining surface from which all the old, precious accumulation had been swept. He, too, he understood, belonged in the thin shadow of the wainscotting. There, dust gave the cautious sojourner a surface to grip. He was pleased with Miss Loyd's rolltop desk. Substantial, unprogressive, it seemed a credential offered for her character. He approved the gallery of snapshots and studio poses of nephews and brothers and nieces along the top, the half-mended glove, lying on the blotter, that she had put aside as he came in, the glimpse he had, through the glass doors of a cupboard, of a hot plate and a brown enamel coffee pot. There were five carnations in a silver jug just below the photograph of the rural seat, and the sixth she wore pinned to the shoulder of her dress, bits of fern and some sort of leaf ruffling softly about the deeper than flesh pink of the flower, setting it off just as the neck of her dress, ruffled and high, seemed intended as the proper foliage to set off her thick, coppery hair and delicate face.

She was tall, he had seen when she rose to greet him, tall as he was himself, though he had not a great height for a man. She was not thin, but not quite plump enough, either, to have been described as opulent—a description, anyway, that was generally applied to an age she had long since passed. She seemed to him wonderfully herself. The soft, dull dress, the flowers: the first hung back on its hanger, the others perhaps left tonight in their jug—he could not, simply, picture them *going on* without her. So it was with her office. His own office, even the executive offices of his firm, with their carefully chosen leather chairs and end tables for lamps and magazines, possessed no stamp of their occupants. The general staff of accountants, file clerks, P.B.X. girls, changed not rapidly but continually, and now and again among the executives one died or moved up or out, and someone else sat in the excellently upholstered swivel chair;—there was no shock of change. The desks and files, the magazines and tables and lamps, belonged to no one, expressed nothing more insistent than the company's satisfactory rating with Dun and Bradstreet. He could not visualize anyone else coming into this office of Blanche Loyd's to take over her business; he could not imagine any continuing for her own desk and chairs and cupboard and hot plate should she ever retire: she held them all together, gave them, through herself, their meaning; without her, they would disintegrate.

And did she now intend to leave them? Was that behind the intention to sell the house in Grant Street? She had been in business here in the Bruce Building, she had told him, for over thirty years; that was a long time. They would go back, perhaps, to their rural seat.

"Have you thought of going back?" he asked. "I mean, to your—to Canada?"

"My mother would like to," she said, "but there'd be no one, really, she could stay with—permanently, I mean. Her own sisters—the two that are still living—are widows, like herself, living with sons or daughters, as she does with me—and I'm tied here. She dreams of buying back the old place, but Lindley—that's my cousin whose father bought the farm from us—Lindley loves it far more passionately than ever we did. He would never sell. She'll be buried there, of course—but for the rest, I suppose it's talk: the things one plans to do in a future that fortunately never comes any closer."

"Like my buying this house of yours," said Mr. Komar. "I've thought about a place of my own for years, until it was hardly even a dream any more, and certainly not something I thought I'd really do." He broke off and regarded Blanche Loyd seriously. "You can't *tell.* . . ." he assured her.

She smiled, a little . . . a little patronizingly, he thought. "A bell rings?" she suggested.

"Not a bell . . ." He faltered. If not a mental bell that rang, then what was it precisely that set one off? What had made him abruptly decide to make this appointment with Blanche Loyd, to take this hour off from his work and come across town from his office to hers, to offer to buy her house?

"No," he said, "it wasn't a bell."

He saw a frown, perhaps of annoyance at his absurd extension of her metaphor.

"Somebody mentioned your name," he said.

She nodded. "Leroy Bledsoe. He has life insurance with me."

"Yes, Bledsoe."

He scarcely heeded her. He thought of yesterday's dark afternoon, of himself coming into the office, back from one of those interminable auditing jobs that took him, now and then, out of town for a few days or a week (though not so often now; now, thank God, they sent the younger men); he thought of coming into the office, putting his briefcase and hat on the rack in the men's cloakroom while he hung up his coat, and Leroy Bledsoe coming out of the washroom, still buttoning his fly, and clapping him on the shoulder: "Back, eh?" But, no, that was not when it had come.

"Bledsoe," he told Miss Loyd, "said you'd made a remark to him about selling your house, and so I . . ."

He retreated into the vision of yesterday's dark afternoon, while Miss Loyd sat still and evidently impatient in her chair at her old desk in the insurance office, brushing tobacco crumbs off her blotter. But the little bell, or whatever its equivalent had been, did not commence to ring again for him now: he could not describe to her the peculiar sensation that had run through him when Bledsoe, going back with him to their desks in the long outer office, had once more clapped him on the shoulder and said, "Still looking for a place of your own?"

He had been then most aware of being clapped a second time, for ordinarily he was neither the clapped nor the clapping kind, and there was a significance added to the question by this soft thud of Bledsoe's hand. He remembered wondering what had got into Leroy? He learned presently that a raise had got into him, and that Leroy was fishing to find out whether he, Herbert Komar, had got one, too. What a curious thing, he now thought, that Leroy's crude angling had led to his finding himself in this office, confronted with Blanche Loyd and with the possible transaction in Grant Street. Offices (he had not worked forty years without finding this out) were procrustean beds of similar crudities, social tactics lopped of their subtleties in order to be accomplished between eight-thirty and five, and no one, in his experience, was fuller of lighthearted malice than the man who had just got a raise and who hoped that the good fortune was his alone;—but these tiny campaigns, these excursions into the territory of allies, were limited things: either way, having accomplished or failed in their objective, they soon flagged. What, then, had made this campaign of Leroy Bledsoe's so utterly different in its outcome? Not Leroy or his method; no, rather, something in himself, Herbert Komar, something that said "Now" when Leroy, still raptly fishing, told him that his insurance agent, an old gal in the Bruce Building, was thinking of selling her house, and that when she'd described it he'd thought, "That's just the place for Komar, if he's got the cash to swing it."

"He has a long memory," said Mr. Komar to Blanche Loyd. She looked puzzled and he elaborated. "Leroy Bledsoe. I haven't said anything to him about buying a house for years."

Miss Loyd turned her eyes away from his, as if she found his accumulated references to buying and selling neither appropriate nor in good taste. She said, "It's a very old house, and Grant Street—isn't what it was once."

"I'll know," he told her confidently. "When I see it, I'll know. They built good houses in those days, not these gimcrack affairs they slap together now."

"And," she went on, fumbling a pencil beneath her spread fingers, "there's a very old woman sitting in it."

She looked at him, quickly, and then away, and the pencil dropped to the floor and rolled between them. He bent down and reached for it, and above him he heard her say, swiftly:

"There's the trouble."

"Trouble?" He straightened up, red-faced.

"Thank you. Old people . . ." she vaguely went on, her eyes just not meeting his.

"Old people?"

She looked away so suddenly that he at once guessed it was to hide her irritation at his obtuseness.

He said, "You mean your mother might not want to sell? She's attached to the house?"

"Attached; yes. Old and attached."

"But so much room!" he exclaimed, thinking of the size of the house as Blanche Loyd had described it to him; thinking, too, of what the coal bill must be, of the incessant city dust that, in so much space, must surely be hard to keep up with; thinking of electric bills, of plumbing, painting, taxes; of the roof that Miss Loyd assured him would have to be reshingled. "And an invalid," he went on. "Now, in an apartment—"

"But who would take care of her?" she interrupted. "In a small apartment there'd scarcely be room for two of us."

"It wouldn't need to be that small," he pointed out reasonably; "or, you could get a woman in during the day."

"Daily help is expensive," she said. "No one wants the care of an invalid."

"Not more expensive, surely, than a couple?" He thought of the possible upkeep the couple she had "living in" must entail.

"Middle-aged couples are glad of a home," she remarked shortly. "They are invariably eccentric, and invariably defeated—not by life but by their own indolence. In a large house one can get away from them, and get some relief from their quirks." She smiled, and added, rather more mildly, "We have never had a housekeeper, for instance, who was not afraid to go down in the basement after dark. Invariably they spot something lurking behind the furnace. Our present housekeeper Mrs. Mentone believes in poltergeists, and has added vampires to her list since I told her my brothers used to play at Dracula in the attic. She won't go up there alone now, or stay with mother at night if I am out and her husband is out, too. She was in show business," she added, as if this aberration accounted for a good deal. "At any rate," she concluded, "people like the Mentones are the good the ill wind of the depression has brought us—brought mother and me, at least, but I am not so sure it would blow anyone very suitable into an apartment."

"The depression won't last forever," he said.

"My mother is old," she reminded him.

It was the kind of remark people did make—"Well, Mother's getting on," or, "Pa won't be with us forever"—but it took on just then a cynicism that seemed neither expected nor appropriate, coming from this woman who impressed him as admirable in so many ways, and who had been, he gathered, a daughter gladly dutiful, providing her invalid mother with a home, a living, and even people to look after her. For a moment he wavered; flung in his lot with the mother, who was old, "old and attached," who did not want to give up the house she had lived in nearly forty years, ever since she left the rural seat and moved across the lake.

"And blind, you said?"

"Blind, too," Blanche Loyd agreed.

Blind, too, poor old thing. He had an instant's vision of Mrs. Loyd sitting quite alone in a chair in a dusty shaft of sunlight, her hands motionless in her lap, an intent expression on her creased and crumpled face as she listened to the sound of footsteps echoing on bare boards in distant, unattainable rooms.

"What does she do?"

"She has the radio: she hears the serials and sends"—a disconcerting note of scorn ruffled the low, smooth voice—"for pictures of the characters. Now and again we get one of the talking books from the blind society."

He thought of the old Mrs. Loyd living now, through her radio, a hundred lives in the hundred radio serials that went on, he knew, all day long, living all those hundred lives because there was no longer any life of her own to live.

"Have you talked about selling?"

"We've talked about it," Miss Loyd said.

"And she? . . ."

"She's strong! Don't think . . . well, I don't know what you may have been thinking; but I can tell you she hasn't lost her wits."

"And what does she say?"

"She admits it is the only thing for us to do."

"Then why do you think she'll make trouble?"

"Because she's never given in, never given in—to life," she brought out, "to the way things are."

"Yet," he said, "she agrees with you."

"She is a great strategist."

And could one blame the old woman? he wondered. There, in that house in Grant Street that was tumbling around her ears, was her last ditch; could one blame her for a ferocious cunning?

"I suppose she *is* fierce about it?" he said.

"I leave you to decide," said Miss Loyd, "when you see her."

"What about your brothers?" he asked. (She had said there were three of them, all much younger than she, living scattered through the state.) "How do they feel?"

"They agree that we will have to sell."

"Does your mother listen to them?"

"My mother perfectly sees the need, Mr. Komar. The last time I brought the matter up, a month or so ago, she talked quite cheerfully of settling into a little apartment."

"You haven't mentioned it since then?"

"Not to her, no."

"She may have thought it over."

Miss Loyd smiled. "She thought it over long before ever I mentioned it."

"Yet," he said, "if she was so willing to give up that"—he nodded at the photograph of the rural seat in Canada—"which surely meant more to her than this house can . . . it seems like a fuss over nothing, doesn't it?"

"She was younger then," Miss Loyd said.

It was undeniable, he thought, that Mrs. Loyd had been younger, but if she was now eighty she had been certainly a mature woman when she made that earlier decision forty years before. "More resilient?" he asked, approaching this explanation from the only angle that seemed tenable.

"More innocent," supplied Miss Loyd.

Ah! innocent! At her words, dark shutters were thrown open with a hard, resistant clank, and from among those green and, in their reasons, fertile distances which lay exposed he did not know which to choose. Which of them had destroyed that pretty rural innocence?

"Money," he murmured. Money, surely, was always at the root of one's lost innocence: either the lack of it or its too great plenty.

"Money," echoed Miss Loyd; but did she agree with him?

"And growing old," he went on.

"Growing old," said Miss Loyd.

"Losing her sight," he said, "not able to walk."

She only smiled; it occurred to him, fleetingly, that somewhere in this enumeration he had wandered from the seductions that drew off innocence. He would have liked to say to Blanche Loyd—though, God knew, it was no business of his, and the curiosity was unnatural in him—"And what else? What really happened?" But she may have guessed his question; he'd noticed that she had a kind of small intuition, picked one up rather sharply now and again; for she said once more:

"You will know when you see her."

"Then you think it's worth going ahead?" he asked; for he had begun to wonder whether his trip across town, his taking this hour out from his work, had not been waste. It was not that he was, as the expression went, a very busy man; it was, more humbly and sharply, that he was someone's employee, an accountant in a large firm, and would be expected to make up his lost time; yes, to tack the hour on at the end of his long day; and he liked his evenings to himself, his evenings in the quiet room he rented at Mrs. Hlavaty's. "You think I should come out?" he said.

She displayed again that curious elusiveness. "Whatever you decide."

"Well." He pushed his glasses back up on his nose and regarded her uncertainly. "Since you leave it to me, and since I've gone this far . . ."

He thought himself through the house in Grant Street as she had described it: eight rooms—five bedrooms, a living room and dining room, and a smaller front parlor, plus an entrance hall, a kitchen and pantry, and a back hall. And Grant Street:

what had she said?—Grant Street wasn't what it had been. He did not know the northwest part of the city very well. "You say the street has gone down?"

"Gone a long way down," Miss Loyd replied.

He got up, groped for his hat. "I live on the south side. We've never got very far up over there. I may not take such a dim view."

"Factories?" asked Miss Loyd, and checked herself as if she were about to make a further identification of the south side.

He nodded. He thought of the harshly lit, straight running, glistening streets of the south side, interspersed with narrow, unpaved or badly paved cul-de-sacs that ended in railway cuttings or factory fences, and were lined with wooden double houses, stucco bungalows, renovated farmhouses, sometimes a grocery store fronted with imitation brick.

"I was brought up over there," he said; "closer to town than I live now, though. But it's all the same, all the way out. Then," he buttoned his overcoat, for it was raw and cold, that Friday in November, 1938, "I'll run over some night. Almost any night would do for me."

"Monday?" she asked. "That will give me a little time—to prepare her."

"I'm sorry," he said slowly, thinking of his vision of the solitary old woman sitting upright and tensely expectant in the house on the street that was no longer very good, "sorry this will be so hard on her. I wish"—he paused—"I wish there were some way I could see the house first, before you tell her. Then, if it isn't suitable for my purpose, there would be no need for her to be upset."

In the silence that followed Blanche Loyd did not look up at him from her desk. She carefully straightened out the fingers on the half-mended glove. She said, "I could tell her you were coming to see me about insurance on your car."

He knew that the strategy had been in her mind before he spoke.

Strategy. He did not like either the crudity of her plan or the deception it involved. It was an ugly thing to do to fool a blind and crippled woman, ugly because it would be, he thought, so very simple. If he could have come as an ordinary caller? . . . But, of course, that was impossible: they would at once be involved in explanations as to why Mrs. Loyd had never heard of him, and why he had suddenly turned up. No, he did not like the plan, but still he saw the practicality of it. Perhaps, he thought, it was really a kind deception? His intention had been kind.

"That's all right, I suppose," he agreed. He went over to the hallway door. "Your mother may find the threat worse than the actuality."

"She's strong," Miss Loyd repeated. "Don't"–she checked herself again; and then, finally, went on–"don't expect too much."

No, he thought, going along the marble hallway and then down the elevator and out into the thin, icy mist of a November rain, he would not expect too much. Life, he thought comfortably, pulling his muffler closer around his neck (he had a delicate throat and suffered from catarrh), had taught him that, that it is better never to expect, never to plan.

Once, painting a deck chair for Mrs. Hlavaty, he had had his vision of what life was like. He had been squatting on the back porch in the hot, full afternoon sun, with newspapers spread carefully on the floor, and the deck chair, stripped of its canvas, set up on the papers, and his paint pot on the papers, too; and slowly, carefully, he had pulled the wet brush down the strips of wood, smoothing out waves in the cream-colored enamel, wiping up with a cloth the drops that fell on the still-unpainted surfaces. And one of those little insects, that are like a mosquito but do not either sing or sting, had settled on the wet paint, and struggled a moment, and, or so it seemed, died. He tore a corner off a newspaper, and lifted the insect out of the paint, and rolled it in the paper and threw the wad into the bushes. Then, with his brush, he went over the smear that marked the spot where the insect had died. And he thought, though he was as good a Catholic as any man who hasn't a wife to prod him into church, that the paint and the brush were the way of Providence, or God, or whatever word you wanted to use, and that the insect's way had been man's. The brush, the divine will, moving impersonally across the wood, intent only on the large accomplishment of the chair, had wished the insect no ill; and he, Herbert Komar, the wielder, had no desire to snatch it out of the air and kill it between his palms. Had it gone its way, carefully, warily, it could have lived its span. But it had made bold; perhaps it had seen the shining surface and something in it had made it go there, and light, and lighting, die; and so it was cast off, and the smooth brush washed across the mark it had made, and that was all. The requiem was the flow of paint across the wooden strip, and the regrets—there were none. So it had been, he thought that day (it was only last summer), in the years of his own life. He had seen men aim too high, reach for the brightness; seen them flaunt . . . flaunt what? he wondered; well, flaunt the way things were; seen them bold and even, sometimes, courageous; he had watched them fall back; yes, and he had watched them die, and the smooth brush had moved on, and the regrets—like the memories, after a moment there were none.

But buying a house, he told himself as he swung off the bus and made his way along the crowded, wet block to his office building, was a different thing, involving no daring, certainly, and surely not aiming too high. He had money in the bank for a house at a modest price; he had a plan for the future—to turn the large house in Grant Street into small housekeeping apartments for students at the university; but even if this plan failed, or he changed his mind about it, he had money enough still to let him see his way ahead. He, too, he thought rather buoyantly, could afford a housekeeping "couple." Yes, he could go ahead; he had no one to think of except himself, no dependents, no wife or chick or aging mother. Mrs. Hlavaty might be disturbed at first, when she learned that she was losing her dependable boarder of ten years; his sister Sadie might think he had lost his mind, wanting a home at his time of life; but these were his only ties. And so he would make a plunge, go to see Blanche Loyd on Monday night, and he even thought there might be some adventure to be got out of his pose as a buyer of insurance. And if he liked the house . . . well, the old lady's fierce attachment to it was her daughter's problem. If he liked the house, he would make his bid, and then sit back and wait, quietly, in the full knowledge that there were plenty of other large, old, cheap houses on the market. At sixty, time, which he understood ought really to have been closing up on him, seemed to be endless. There was no need to get in a rush. But he rather thought that this was the house; he, too, had an intuition, and was just superstitious enough to find an extra meaning in Leroy Bledsoe's having run into him there in the cloakroom and remembering that casual remark of his about starting a boarding house, made a long time ago.

Over the weekend he thought often of the house in Grant Street, though he did not mention the plan to his fellow lodgers, but just as often, or more so, his thoughts turned to the rural seat in Canada—turned in curiosity as something, however remotely, touching him. The place in Grant Street he had seen no picture of, but that was not why some kind of image of it eluded him. All the houses built fifty or sixty years before looked, he knew, like all the other houses built around the same time. It would sit up high on its high foundation, square and sturdy, with not enough windows for the great stretches of wall. There would be a porch across the front of it, and wooden steps going down to the sidewalk. Perhaps it would have some jigsaw frills around the eaves, and some stained glass, or a bay window and a corner tower. It would look, in fact, not unlike the house he lived in now, Mrs. Hlavaty's. It was this very expected commonness of it that kept him from fixing it in his mind. But the house in Ontario that lay a few miles back from the town that was too much like a vacation spot in this country—that house over there had an ugly individuality that it would have been difficult not to keep an image of.

He wondered, as he remembered its unpromising lines, what kind of family loved a house so passionately that they would not give it up? The families he knew lived in a double house or an apartment until they got something ahead, and then they bought a suburban colonial with six rooms and a breakfast nook; and there they stayed unless they came into a windfall, in which case they moved into what was called a French Norman structure with a tower over the front door; when one of them died off, the place was sold, and the surviving member went to live with a married son or daughter. And that was that: somebody else with something put away moved into the colonial and ate in the breakfast nook, or welcomed in guests at the door in the Norman tower. As for others that he knew, men or women like himself, they lived in rented rooms, as he did, or shared walk-up apartments with friends, or stayed at an apartment hotel, or, less often, bought a double or a duplex and rented the other half in order to pay off the mortgage. And when, in their turn, they died or grew old, either they lost the house because the mortgage lapsed, or they sold it and took their money and went to live with an elderly cousin who had a cottage at St. Petersburg or a house at Loudonville, Ohio.

What kind of family, now, hung onto a house that, so Blanche Loyd had told him, they had built somewhere back in the seventeen hundreds? He did not know. He could not even guess what motivated such an attachment. If it had been one of those southern places that you saw pictures of in travel folders and decorating magazines, then he might have understood how they felt. But the rural seat in the yellowing photograph had no two-story columns, no spreading wings and sheltered, side verandas, no curving outside stairways and handsome gardens. It was long, low, unpainted, with shaggy fieldstone chimneys at either end and what might be an attic under its peaked roof. It had no formal façade at all: among the three doors scattered irregularly along its front he could not remember one that seemed more of a principal entrance than another. It had no veranda, only three little stone stoops outside each of the undistinguished doors. It sat on a bare rise of ground, with a few trees leaning uncertainly against one corner, and a pasture fence running all along the front of it to keep the cows from wandering into the parlor–if, beyond one of those doors, there was a parlor.

Since he continued, in spite of his rationalizations, to hesitate slightly before the deception that he and Miss Loyd proposed to practice on Mrs. Loyd, he thought that perhaps, if he could understand the family attachment to this other house, he would know how Mrs. Loyd might be reached, how persuaded that her feeling for the place in Grant Street was foolish in an age when people flew like shuttlecocks from dwelling to dwelling, and went on living and thriving and, ultimately, dying, but not dying for love of a lost house.

But he could not do it. He, who had lived everywhere, first in that drafty cottage in Lark Street, with his parents and his sister, then in the double house with Momma, after Poppa died, and later still, after Momma was put in the Home, in a succession of rented rooms of which the latest was this one at Mrs. Hlavaty's –he could not understand what kind of lasting sentiment could attach itself to a building that was merely old, merely a shell in which some generations of farmers had lived and died. Home is you, he thought, not at all intending a sanctimony. So he had found it, taking his pleasure in putting his suits and robes and shoes and pajamas in the succession of closets opening off the innumerable rooms he had occupied, laying his brush and bottle of shaving lotion on the bureau, putting his toothbrush in the bathroom. And if now he wanted a place of his own? Not sentiment, not at all: he wanted simply to settle down and to wait, undisturbed by the inquiring eyes of a landlady and fellow boarders, to wait with his eyes peacefully closed for comfortable age to settle along his stiffening arms and legs. There was something awful and sad about old men dying in rented rooms;

far better that they expire in their own beds in their own homes. And he was in a position now . . .

"I am in a position now," he murmured, lying Sunday night in his rented bed, "to afford . . ."

And he fell heavily, instantly, asleep.

• 2 •

THE HOUSE was in Canada, miles from Grant Street and the dense, semiurban thicket stretching all around it, separated from Grant Street not only by the miles, and by the chunky, distended body of water that was Erie, but by the years. Time lay opaque between the two, Mr. Komar knew later: time eternally kept the two separate, the rural seat in Canada, and Grant Street; no boat could cross its pale waters, or trains run round its endless, endlessly stretching brim;—and, anyway, Mary Bush was dead, lost to him irretrievably in one of those absolute sinkholes in time.

There was the fact of himself, too, that he did not know how to counter the past gracefully, how even to do that much. The past, as he was sometimes to see it through the Loyds' eyes, was a kind of garment that lent not so much luster as vital being to its wearer. From him it had been stripped. The Loyds' pointing out how he strutted naked and absurd before them was perhaps the only demonstrable fact that, until the end, they gave him, though through his encounter with them he was to be told again and again of the daughter's wonderful honesty, her rigid adherence to the truth. The mother was not so honest; she scorned the vulgar truth that sprang only from the phenomenal reality, and in the end he was to think her more nearly correct, and Blanche wrong. But on that Sunday night in November, 1938, when he dropped off to sleep, he did not know Lily Loyd and, of course, he knew nothing of Mary Bush, who was to speak to him neither out of truth nor out of the long fiction that the house in Grant Street enclosed, but out of the dream that began sometime the day that Leroy Bledsoe, buttoning up his fly, came out of the washroom and unexpectedly clapped him on the shoulder.

Through it all the image of the house in Grant Street was, as the larger argument firmed itself, to remain still without substantiality, though he came shortly to know almost every part of it: its rooms, their furnishings. There was, as the principal set, the living room with its two great arches and their sliding doors—the one heavy door, which now was permanently closed, leading into the front hall, and the other, at right angles to it, into the dining room. Here in the living room, in a tapestry chair, sat Lily Loyd, in front of the fireplace that straddled the corner between the two great doors. Here, in her old brass double bed, she slept, having grown too heavy to be carried daily from one floor to the other. Here, too, she performed those other, less engaging, functions that were always referred to obliquely: "Mother would like to be put over on her Chair." For there was no bathroom on the first floor. Alongside the closed-off doorway into the hall was the cot where Blanche had slept ever since her mother's life had contracted into this one room. On it she lay down at night, her mother eight feet away across the floor in her brass bed, and they were silent in their antagonisms, or, less often, vehement in their recriminations. There was a semblance of peace during those infrequent intervals when Mrs. Mentone occupied the cot in order to give Blanche a night or two of undisturbed rest in her own room upstairs. The flame died briefly down.

In front of the side window and almost at the foot of Lily's bed was the rocker in which, in that other house across the lake and that other time, Mary Bush had pieced together the innumerable squares of the hundred Stars of Bethlehem and Double Wedding Rings she had made. Her portrait hung on the wall behind Lily's chair, cracked and fading; but still her eyes were—ah! he thought, so blue. On the lower shelf of the pilastered and mirrored mantel was another picture: Lily Loyd in a silver frame.

Her fierce eyes, Mr. Komar often thought, seemed to meet across the corner of the room those eyes of Mary Bush—and was a look exchanged, he wondered, between the woman in the photograph, in pearls and a lace collar, and the woman in the portrait painted long ago by a peripatetic artist?

"I am Mary Bush," said the woman in the painting.

"I am Lily Loyd," said the photograph.

But the woman who sat still but not at rest beneath them in the tapestry chair, the woman whose photograph that was on the mantel, made twenty years ago when she was sixty: what response did she make?

"I have kept no faith except anger."

She told him that, there at the very end; but her observation was, he thought, an example of the truth, and how the truth, in this particular case, invariably distorted, invariably was itself all wrong.

So the living room.

The other rooms engaged him less imperiously, though several of them were the scenes of minor skirmishes, sudden clarities, abrupt defeats: the front hall with its hat rack that climbed to the ceiling, and the dancer on the newel post; the small, crowded back hallway with its staircase that rose into cold dark (here it was, Mrs. Mentone told him, that the red ball waited at night, when she and Lily sat alone in front of the gas fire; oh, yes, she could hear the ball swing open the door at the head of the steps, and pause there with a slow breath, and then swing itself lumberingly down).

He came to know the densely furnished parlor, too, where he saw the snowstorm globe that had cracked; and the landing of the massive front staircase, where the Loyds had hung a frail, faded sketch of the rural seat that was, in its way, a portent of the end. He came to know even the bedrooms and, though he did not see it, the dark, low attic in which the Loyd children had played, with the black trunk under a far eave which had figured in their resurrection of Dracula. Mrs. Mentone believed that he lingered, unexorcised and unexorcisable, up there still, moving with a mothlike stealth among the rafters, consolidating into the dressmaker's form in the front windows or stooping low behind a gilt frame, where his red and flaring eyes could be seen peering out of the mild features of some forgotten great-ancestor. There were children in the neighborhood who said that the house was haunted, and indeed it did seem that the phenomena of a restless non-mortality lingered everywhere: basement, attic, stairways.

Yes, he knew the passageways and the high, square rooms of the house as well or better than he ever knew the interior of Mrs. Hlavaty's home; but still the house was only a field for the argument that raged among the inmates, and drew him in, too, and, through him, Mary Bush, who had been dead these forty years, and who was no part of his own sad and ramshackly past. Ah! there was the beauty of it: that through him, the outsider, she at last made plain, across the years, across the momentous century, her vision. And it came to seem to him appropriate that the sale of a house should, as it were, have set them all off, for the Loyds had always been intimately bound up with their own dwellings; he was to learn that the spirit of the *voyageur* was strong in each of them, too, but that the instinct to seek shelter, the desire to build furniture, to fill up rooms with the accumulation of generations of occupancy—that these were stronger in them still. So they had built once in Manhattan; and then moved on across the Jersey marshes and built again; and he felt certain that the tents they erected on the long rafts that took them, years later, up the track of the St. Lawrence and into Ontario country, had been furnished, too. Yes, they had traveled, but at every stage they had erected around them walls: of stone, canvas, log. Their collective epitaph might have read, "They Dwelt. . . ."

In that one way, at least, as holders of houses and of land, they were always clear to him, always the representatives of the past, while he, the wandering dweller within the rented, anonymous walls, was, he thought, the dislocated present. Beyond those margins there were uglier definitions, but it was, again, just the beauty of the situation that he, the outsider, could set himself up to redefine, and, in redefining, to reaffirm—in fact, to present fresh—the vision of Mary Bush.

While increasingly, then, the clapboard house in Grant Street only diminished in importance and vitality, his image of the rural seat in Canada grew into a spectral shape larger than definition, more complexly and urgently present than any shape of mortal reality; he could not reach it: he was at once too innocent and not innocent enough, too knowing, too little learned. It had for him, in the weeks to come, the shape of hyperbole, inexact, devastating: and where was the meaning of it? He thought the meaning lay in its mistress, the lady of the blue eyes, Mary Bush. In the house in Grant Street he watched her portrait: there she sat in the chipped gold frame, a piece of something thrown across her silk lap, just the thin, spiky glimmer of a needle, the insubstantial gleam of a thread to show that she was supposed to be sewing; and behind her, brimming up, the brownish-golden light that is always the light of the century that is not ours. (The lady beneath the portrait, in the tapestry chair, sat in no such rich illumination: poor Lily! only lit up by the glow of a General Electric light bulb.) And when he was away from Grant Street Mary Bush swept, boldly and quite at odds with his conscious intention, free of the plaster frame, free of her needle and the silk skirt and the bit of stuff that she pushed her needle through. She ran . . . where did she run? He longed to look, and was afraid, and then, looking, saw that after all the light was not good: she had radiantly gone. But he could follow? Through the rural seat he could learn her secret? He looked toward the extended, disconcerted façade. The image of it was strong: he almost felt the wind blowing down off Hudson Bay, stirring the chestnut and oak in the north quarter, ripping across the willow islands, leveling the sea of swale west of the house. The tiny, mottled panes caught the last of the sun thickly and seemed to repel the dark. Someone opened the pasture gate; beyond a door frame a dim figure moved intent. The abrupt darkness came; and, no, the house told him nothing. Its assertion was unmistakable; he caught at its beauty: light flickered at a pane; he ran there, but he could not see in; somewhere, a door opened; frantically, he looked, but they were all shut, all stolid. He slipped and clawed at the sides; now the house seemed enclosed away from him, encased in a snowstorm globe, and, despairing, he caught up the globe and heaved it, but the intact perfect interior, exposed to the air, disintegrated, and among the shards he found nothing, no scrap of cloth, no splinter of wood; and looking up he looked into the blind, white-disked eyes of Lily Loyd, who said, "I have kept no faith except anger." And he said piteously, "What will become of us?"—but, no, it was the housekeeper who spoke, Annabelle Mentone; the shattered present was broken by voices crying "Shame!", crying, "There's nothing for you here; nothing, nothing!"—insistently reproaching him back into the tenuous reality, cutting under the hyperbole that he too only seemed to destroy, insistent in their destruction of the dream he could not grasp, could not, alone, save; could only love.

PART TWO

The Visit

· 3 ·

Even at eight o'clock in the evening, and on a rainy night like this, the traffic along Grant Street was heavy. The street had suffered the customary fate of east-west thoroughfares in a city growing chiefly in those directions: it had become a throughway to the farther suburbs; it had cracked, peeled; in Blanche Loyd's phrase, it had gone down. Progress is merciless and undiscriminating, and that Grant had once been a fine street, that it had meant something to live on it, did not perturb the truck drivers who hauled their heavy loads in and out of the downtown area along its length, or the urban bus companies who had erected their little, triangular signs along the sidewalks. The more acute and less sentimental residents had long ago moved away, following the east-west trend, and into the houses had come a swarm of vagrants—millworkers, stenographers, cleaning-women, young men from the stripped and ruined fringes of West Virginia. The damage this crop of locusts had done was still confined chiefly to the lower end of Grant Street, but even at the western end, where the Loyds lived, there was evidence that the decline was coming on fast: a drugstore built on the front of a house, a sign offering sleeping rooms, a fire escape running down a wall past the long-ago pride of a stained-glass landing window. And one by one the trees—that surest index of a street's repute—were coming down too.

Mr. Komar's Chevrolet crept along close to the curb, the traffic rocketing and booming past it. He swung the car spotlight toward the row of houses on his right. "Come up Kingery,"

Miss Loyd had suggested when he telephoned her Saturday morning at her office. "It's a slightly longer route, but not so busy after the rush hour. There's a Methodist Church at the corner of Grant, and a drugstore across from it; and the intersection has a stoplight, so you can't get lost. Turn right, and we're in the second long block, on the right side."

This was the second block. "8119," he read. "8117." It would be farther up ahead, in all likelihood; but he continued to drive slowly on the chance that the numbers skipped, as they did on his own street. He was, further, a good deal curious about Grant. It retained still, at this end, a dignity, a suggestion of space, solidity—even, though with ragged nerve-ends showing, of determined imperturbability in the face of the incessant activity along its pavement. If the houses needed paint, they were still in good order; if their front lawns had been chopped off by successive widenings of the street, still they possessed generous sideyards, and down their driveways he had glimpses of immense depths of backyard.

He swung the spotlight again. It fell full on the face of a woman who was walking toward him. She plodded along the sidewalk in a dark coat and with a white scarf over her head, as indifferent, apparently, to the brief celebrity of the light as she seemed to be to the insistent rain. But Mr. Komar was embarrassed. Oh, dear, he thought, she'll think I'm a masher. He wrenched the light sharply upward. It played among the scattered branches overhead; up and up it went, into the spacious nighttime sky, turning the heavy raindrops into brilliant crystals. But a bus whirled past him, sounding its horn, and he was obliged to attend to his driving. Carefully, he aimed the light once more at the row of houses. "8111."

The porch light was on at the next house. Could that be it? No: a row of cars, he saw coming opposite, filled the drive. Somebody was having a party. He thought he would enjoy living on a street where people had parties. And he liked the idea of neighbors running in and out, in to borrow a light bulb, back to answer their phone that shrilled across the intervening yard. "I thought I had a sixty-watt, but when I looked . . . was that my phone? . . ." That kind of fleeting, undemanding contact that he everywhere looked for, but sustained over the days and nights, over the years, as it was not now: for restaurant help had a way of going off to other jobs, and one had then the difficult business of starting all over again; and most of the other guests in Mrs. Hlavaty's house moved indifferently on, sooner or later.

Of course, life at Mrs. Hlavaty's was not completely isolate. Now and again Mrs. Hlavaty had a few friends in for the evening, and invited him downstairs. They played Hearts until about ten, and then she served coffee and tuna fish salad sandwiches. But the occasions were, somehow, *labored*, he thought, not swift and bright; they had no energy. Mrs. Hlavaty seemed to know few of the residents along her street beyond that kind of acquaintance that obliged her to recognize them when they met in the grocery store or at church. Her evening groups were made up from an invariable and not much larger group that went all the way back to her high school days, and that lived scattered through the city and suburbs, so that the parties ended early: everyone had a long drive in front of him, and no one was as young as he used to be.

Ten years of tuna fish salad sandwiches, he thought, suddenly aghast at his own fortitude. "Thank you for a very pleasant evening, Mrs. Hlavaty. I surely enjoyed myself. Can I help you with the card table?"

"Well, everybody seemed to enjoy themselves, didn't they, Mr. Komar? Just put it behind the kitchen door. Oh, my! All those dishes. No, no, now; I'm just going to rinse them off. I'll do them tomorrow."

Still, it was kind of her to ask him to her evenings. The only other boarder she entertained was Miss Kasco, who had been in the house almost as long as he had, and Miss Kasco did not come whenever she and Mrs. Hlavaty were having one of their misunderstandings. When they were, Miss Kasco would stomp out of her room just as the guests began to arrive, and into the bathroom, and then back to her room and *slam* went her door. The next morning at breakfast she would look pale, and pinched around her sharp, abundant nose, and she would sniff the stale, tobacco-ridden air that was the last vestige of the party, and cough a little, critically. Miss Kasco was sensitive to smoke, and opposed to it on principle, for she was a civics teacher at the high school. He sometimes thought it a pity that she was not more sensitive to other public nuisances, for she used a very strong toilet water. He believed it was gardenia. When she got upset—and she was a poor loser at the card table—the toilet water seemed to explode from every pore.

"8037." Yes, it would be nice to live on a street where there was a lot of coming and going among the residents. Naturally, the boarders at Mrs. Hlavaty's couldn't very well have parties in their bedrooms, and while Mrs. Hlavaty said they were perfectly welcome to use the living room some evening if they wanted to have guests, no one ever seemed to do it.

"If you ask *me*," Miss Kasco said to him one night, meeting him as he came out of the bathroom, "she'd"—she hesitated—"she'd blow her *top*"—(she brought out the colloquialism as if it were superb and profane, and indeed it was startling to hear it bounding out of the lady's otherwise aggressively correct vocabulary)—"blow it right *off*," she added, "if we really wanted to use that room!" And with an embattled flourish of her towel she marched into the bathroom and slammed the door. Of course, Miss Kasco was upset at the time because she'd wanted to have a friend from Indiana to stay with her, and Mrs. Hlavaty had said that while it would be perfectly all right as far as she was concerned, she was afraid the other roomers might be a little put out because of there being only the one bathroom, and goodness knows that bathroom was like Grand Central Station as it was. In deference to Mrs. Hlavaty's tragic concern with "the bathroom situation" Mr. Komar had long ago dropped down to one bath every week and a half. "There's Miss Kasco washing her hair all the time," she'd say; and, "I wish Miss Kasco would remember to rinse out her personal clothing in the basement. It makes a very bad situation for all of us."

These delicate pricks, these confusions and misunderstandings, these tiny wars and grim victories that seemed to him, in the significance given them, out of all proportion to the involved issues ("That is *my* slip on the shower ring, Mrs. Hlavaty. It will be *quite dry* by morning, and then I'll take it *down*"; "You do understand, dear: it isn't that *I'd* mind welcoming your friend—I know how lovely any friend of yours would be—but I'm afraid there might be com*plaints*. . . ."), had been a part of his life not only at Mrs. Hlavaty's but at every other house where he'd ever had a room. But like Mrs. Loyd, he was no longer as resilient as he had once been.

Yet, I haven't minded, he told himself; and knew that rather he had done his best to avoid taking sides or expressing an opinion—and that, in fact, this deliberate negation had often required a strenuous maintenance, and that he had very much minded the effort. In her way, though, Mrs. Hlavaty was a kind and sensible woman, and she had had a hard life. Miss Kasco had her points, too. She was a college graduate, having her degree in education from Bowling Green University, and she subscribed to the Literary Guild. As for the other boarders: they came and went. He and Miss Kasco stayed on, year after year.

"My old standbys," Mrs. Hlavaty often said, and she liked her joke. "*I* saw you and Mildred Kasco coming up the walk together. Now, Mr. Komar, you're too *old* for that!" If this was irritating, he found it also, at times, a little touching. Here was Mrs. Hlavaty's own small and hesitant tentacle put out. Unlike him, she was not satisfied with the brief and public contact: it was well enough for him to eat her tuna fish, drink her coffee, sit at her card table, well enough as far as it went; but she wanted something more, something deeper and charged with a continuing life: she wanted emotion. If he would not give it to her, she would manufacture it, using whatever material came to hand: if it was only something she made up, still it was a band between them, and willy-nilly she would draw him in. He forgave her, except when she had the execrable unwisdom to jolly him in Mildred Kasco's presence. The effect on Miss Kasco was nothing short of deplorable. She went off into gales of laughter, and her gardenia toilet water broke over him like a cloudburst. "I'm going to lock my *door!*" she'd gasp; and Mrs. Hlavaty would smile and shake her head, her face rosy with the pleasurable indiscretion: "Oh, my land! Aren't *we* a fine bunch!" She was briefly satisfied: the band was forged; but it would be hours before Miss Kasco was back to normal.

Still, they were both ladies. You never heard an off-color word from either of them, the way you did from some of the girls around the office. "If they were my girls," he'd said more than once to Mr. Perry at the next desk, "I'd take them home and wash their mouths out." Mr. Perry always shook his head, and adjusted his sleeve garters higher on his thin arms, and said, "I know it! I know it!"

He was no longer resilient. That was the trouble, and a sudden great irritation with the strictures of life in a rooming house had come on him with the discovery. Beyond his bedroom door there was no privacy: he bathed in the pale glare of Miss Kasco's slip, which nightly she washed out and hung across the shower ring to dry. Her denture brush fell to the linoleum floor when he took his own off the holder. Mrs. Hlavaty commented on the number of times he used the bathroom; and Myron Vogel, whose room adjoined his own, always pulled too much paper off the roll, so that as one sat down the ragged lengths that Myron had stored on the toilet top fluttered airily around one's feet, and had to be laboriously collected. "I'm going to get you boys a *paper*-weight," Mrs. Hlavaty had once cried gaily, thinking that Myron was not the only offender.

"8021." Twenty-one . . . once I too was twenty-one, he thought suddenly. He saw himself a young man walking up the gravel path to the house in Lark Street. He heard the streetcar grinding off, and he opened the front door into the parlor, and the smell of cabbage and kidneys cooking, and the green light swimming in the room behind the drawn blinds, made his stomach turn over, sitting in the cold, scentless dark, with the rain falling, flashing his light now here (he saw a woman standing on a porch, arms clasped together high around her chest), now there ("8015," he read). The old sensation formed again, the distaste, the awful hopelessness: Momma, so pitiably thin and dried out, his sister Sadie sitting on the front steps with her slicked-down, sniggering beaux, and Poppa out of one job and into another and out of that one, too—always drinking too much; and himself a payroll clerk at Associated Steel and Wire: leaving the house before it was dawn, coming home so late: only in summer was the green light still left captive in the parlor.

What kind of life was that? Then Poppa dying, and the expense of keeping Momma when she got ill, and Sadie writing her pitiable, proud little requests for money from the southeastern part of the state where she and her first husband had gone in the desperate search for work.

What kind of life? he asked himself. "8001." And in twenty years he'd be what? He'd be in his eighties, too.

How did you know how old you were? How could you tell without a mirror, or without people to say, "At your age you've got to take things easy"? How would you know, now? The years passed—he had read this somewhere: it might be in one of Miss Kasco's books—they passed like searchlights sweeping across the sky: so he flung his own light up again, into the bare, ribbed trees, up: it dissolved into a street light. Into the brightness, he thought, where all things are lost. He thought of Mr. Perry, sitting at his desk, his fingers dancing across the adding machine, saying, "Well, you've got all the time there is." Ah. True. But the years swung, bright at the zenith, then dimming; up went another ray, another year, and who could keep count, each one being so much like the one before? How did you tell? For mirrors lied, or else you forgot really to look at yourself; and people were kind.

The years abruptly consolidated for him, like so many obscure companies merging into a single corporation—and which, achieving that much solidarity, attempted no more, lest in putting too much importance on their joint concern they should discover that their merger had resulted only in a vaster obscurity. Yet, from this consolidation which he dared not look at too closely, or for long, he did extract a particular that summarized not too painfully, and with an irony he was even tempted to appreciate, all those indistinct, those scrupulous, those undistinguished years: —himself in a line at the bank, putting something away every payday, first out of those tiny checks from Associated Steel and Wire, and then a little more after Momma died and Sadie married again; and quite a lot—ten dollars, usually, out of every pay—after he passed his examinations and became a C.P.A. In a line at a bank, he said ("7937"), I have spent my life giving dollars to a teller, and I've had all the time there is. But I would like, he said, I would like to settle down now. Yet, coldly, the thought came to him: what else have I been all these years? "Mr. Komar is very settled in his ways," Mrs. Hlavaty would say. "You don't see him chasing around to bars and poolrooms. Well, I think everybody enjoyed themselves, don't you?"

It would certainly be nice to live on a street where people had parties. He saw ladies in long dresses dancing across driveways, bundled up in rabbit-fur jackets: houses shone brilliantly with lights.

"Make yourselves at home!" he cried, flinging the door open. "I'll put a record on the victrola. Would you care for this foxtrot?"

Home, he thought.

For here he was. "7933." Grant Street.

The porch light was on here, too. As he stopped the car, he saw someone come through the front hall and climb the stairs. A switch was flipped, and the front windows on the second floor caught and held a meager radiance. He pulled his keys out of the ignition and, holding them, looked again at the house.

It differed little from his expectations. It was square and high and set back not very far from the sidewalk. It looked much like the other houses surrounding it, and not unlike Mrs. Hlavaty's home. If it was somewhat superior to its period, it was because, he suspected, it had been built by a family that had not so much money as their neighbors. There were no fretwork frills, no ornate, triangular, paneled pillars supporting the porch roof, and no stained glass, so far as he could see. Shrubberies, massed deep around the porch and all along the walk that led to the side door, did something to root it down, but not enough; it still, on its lofty brick foundation, had a tendency to stretch perilously and clumsily into the sky. If it was not a good-looking house, it was at least a house about which you could say that it would never look worse than it did now.

As he sat there, a woman appeared in the wide window that was far to the right of the front door. She cupped a hand over her face and peered out. He sat tense, the keys on their ring jingling against the steering wheel. He almost believed that his eyes met the woman's, through the rain and dark, colliding on the naked exposure of the lit porch. They were suspended together in a mutuality of tension. It was Blanche Loyd: he recognized even at a distance the square and squarely delicate face, the firm jawline.

A bus swept up beside him and then plunged on into the night; the Chevrolet rocked and jiggled with the motion of its passing. For a moment he could not breathe, and there was no sound in the car except the incessant clatter of the keys against the wheel as his gloved hand rose, paused, fell, and rose again.

The woman at the window straightened and turned. As she did so, she spoke to someone: he saw her lips move. She turned back and lifted her arm, and a shade flopped down. That was queer, he thought. It was as if he had been rudely shut out. He undid the middle button on his overcoat and pulled out his watch. In the street's thin, wet lighting he could just make out that the hands stood at ten minutes until eight. He had overestimated the time it would take to drive over here, and he was ten minutes early. He put the watch back and cleared his throat. He thought he would wait just a little.

"Miss Loyd?" he said.

He was alarmed at the loudness of his voice. The key ring fell away from the wheel. He felt blood pounding in his temples. Well, now, this is foolish, he told himself; and he told himself: she probably didn't even see me, with the porch light on, and so much traffic in the street, anyway.

"Miss Loyd?"

The words caught in his throat. He swallowed hard and tried once more to get it clear. Then, resolutely, abandoning the temptation to delay, he slid across the front seat and got out the door and locked it after him. Rain splashed against his glasses as he went along the sandstone walk that led to the porch steps. The desire to delay was almost compulsive—to delay long enough to explain to himself that odd turning away of hers from the window and the pulling down of the shade, but even more to explain the slow fear that ran cold through him. But he knew he ought to hurry. It would seem a little unusual, his strolling like this through the hard fall, and someone might be looking, observing him through one of those dim glass squares on the second floor. He looked: the house reared lofty against the splashing sky. Did he see a shadow of movement in one of the windows? Or was it water that rolled along his lens? He scuttered the few remaining yards. The steps creaked under his rubbers, and where the treads had hollowed under use, or sagged from damp and rot, he struck puddles: they parted and rose, and splashed over the rims of his rubbers.

He crossed the porch and rang the bell. But no one came. He waited at least a minute, and then pushed the bell again, holding his finger on it until he had counted five—the method he used at the office to ring for the wandering elevators. Through the glass panels in the storm door, beyond the square window in the front door itself, the interior of the house looked bleared, as if he were peering into an aquarium. He pulled off his glasses and wiped them hurriedly between the fingers of his glove. He heard footsteps: someone was coming down the stairway—a woman with slender legs and an enormous body housed in something flowered. He stepped back, but the woman rounded the stair post and went toward the door at the end of the hall.

Quite clearly, above the rain and the quick plunging sounds of automobiles and buses, he heard her call, "Hoo, hoo! Blanche! Somebody's at the door." She hesitated. Then she called, "All right," and turned and came toward him. He stepped forward. He saw the woman struggling with the main door: it trembled, groaned; in the light its timbers seemed to ripple and reverberate like sheet metal. Presently, with a report like a pistol shot, it moved back a little. He opened the storm door and let it rest against his shoulder.

But the woman abruptly stopped tugging, and instead pushed at the door. It crashed into place. Baffled, he drew back. She commenced her struggle again, and with a crack it flew open. She was precipitated backward, and for a moment longer he stood hesitantly on the wet porch.

"That's a mean cuss," she said breathlessly, pulling up a strap under her dress. "Come right in." She held the storm door until he had passed through. "The damp," she explained, still obliged to be almost monosyllabic. She pushed a shaken loop of hair beneath the broad yellow ribbon she wore round her head, and took a deep breath. "Keeps the salesmen off, though. I pull and pull, and then I shake my head and they go away. Did you have to wait long? I thought Blanche was going to answer, but Mrs. Loyd had to—" She broke off.

He felt suddenly relieved, certain that whatever Mrs. Loyd had had to do had been connected with the pulling down of the shade. "Mrs. Loyd?" he said.

"Ah! Got it!" cried the woman. The main door slid into place; she turned the lock. "Her chair," she said, "though I shouldn't tell you that." He must have looked puzzled, for she added hastily,

"You know: no bathroom. Chair, chair." She hastened on over her indiscretion. "Mr. Kramer?"

"Komar."

"Here, let me have your coat. How do you do? I'm Mrs. Mentone. Is it still raining? Blanche said she could hardly see to get off the streetcar tonight. No; just give it to me. I'll put it out on the hook over the register, and it'll be dry by the time you go. I saw a car drive up, but I didn't think it could be yours. Blanche said you wanted to take out some insurance, so I thought you must have a new one."

"I'm—thinking of getting one," he said. He hoped there was no visible quivering of his eyeballs. He glanced quickly away from her. For all the rather distracted good humor about her, she had shrewd eyes, and she did not appear a fool. Her raddled, painted face had a look of hard and extensive experience.

The heat in the front hall seemed to close round him: he felt the blood begin to circulate again; and, thank God, no cabbage, no smell of anything at all.

"Komar," said Mrs. Mentone reflectively, walking away from him with that sort of stately, thrust-forward grace that stout women often achieve. She fitted his coat onto a hanger from the rack beside the stairs. "Do you have any relatives in New Jersey? There was a man who ran a gas station in Montclair when Lou—that's my husband—and I lived there, and his name was Komar."

"No," said Mr. Komar, "all my family's right here in Ohio."

"Well," she said, going toward the short hallway that led into the kitchen, "I don't think that was his real name, anyway. The family'd just shortened it to Komar. It's like that around New York now. Do you know New York? You hear every language except English." In the light from the hall he saw her hang his coat against the wainscotting above the kitchen floor register. "There," she said, returning. "My, you do look cold: you're all pinched around the mouth. I wouldn't be surprised if this turned to snow. Lou's at the Elks tonight, and I told him to take his galoshes." She lifted a lid on the seat of the hat rack and looked inside. "Hah!" she exclaimed. She extracted two galoshes. Their buckles jingled together as she dropped them in again. "What did I tell you?"

Mr. Komar was reminded of his rubbers, and stepping first on the back of one, and then of the other, he got out of them.

"Now you have some sense," said Mrs. Mentone approvingly. "And no woman to look after you?" she asked (Miss Loyd had evidently gone some distance into his history in preparing the household). "Well, some men get along just as good on their own. Put them over here."

There was another iron grating, like the one in the kitchen, in the floor near the front door. He put his rubbers on top of it.

"And here's Blanche!" cried Mrs. Mentone.

He straightened and turned to look through the doorway into the kitchen. Miss Loyd came past the stove, a chair, his swaying coat.

"Good evening. I hope you didn't freeze out there waiting for us to let you in."

Mrs. Mentone said, "We've been having quite a talk. It turns out Lou and I knew a relative of his in . . . Oh, no, you said he wasn't, didn't you? I was saying to Mr. Komar what a small world it is. Lou and I knew a Komar quite well in Montclair."

"I'm afraid I'm early."

"It's just," replied Miss Loyd, "that I had to—to help Mother, and I couldn't get to the door when you rang."

"Well, it gave *me* a start," said Mrs. Mentone. "I went up to get my slippers, and I'd just got my shoes off when I heard the bell. Nobody comes to the front door at night, and you never know. A woman was attacked just a few streets over last month. We've all been jittery. I told Blanche she ought to leave the office early and get home before dark."

"I hardly think," said Blanche Loyd, "that there would be much danger at a lighted front door."

"Ah!" replied Mrs. Mentone mysteriously. "That's exactly where they're so clever."

"I started too soon," he said. "I thought it would take me longer to drive out here."

"Did you get her back?" asked Mrs. Mentone. She looked as if she might laugh, and her eyes avoided Mr. Komar's.

"No, and I wanted to ask you—" Miss Loyd turned to him. "Would you mind waiting a minute more, Mr. Komar?"

"Not at all. I'm sorry to . . ."

"There's no reason. I thought we had Mother settled, and that's the trouble." She and Mrs. Mentone turned toward the door to the kitchen. "I got her over all right," he heard Miss Loyd say, "but I couldn't seem to budge her when she was ready to move back."

"I tell you she's a load," said Mrs. Mentone. "More nights than one I go to bed with stiff shoulders. Lou helps, of course."

"Well, *not?* . . ." Miss Loyd began in a cold voice.

This time Mrs. Mentone gave way. "Oh, no!" she giggled. "You know, at lunchtime, when we take her out to the table."

They disappeared through a door at the end of the kitchen, and Mr. Komar seated himself in a rocker near the newel post. But a draft swept down from the second floor, and he moved to a chair that was placed against a sliding door in the righthand wall. Beyond that door, he judged, was the room where Miss Loyd had pulled the shade over the window, for at his back he could hear low, hurried voices. There was a creaking noise, and then a little shriek. He heard Mrs. Mentone's laugh; someone else—probably Miss Loyd—said, "Shhh!"

He tried not to listen, and concentrated on looking over the hallway. He admired the daisy sprays that sprang across the brown field of the wallpaper. The woodwork was a rich, golden brown, and the stairway massive and solid. On the flat top of the newel post stood the iron figure of a woman in slender draperies, who held aloft a cluster of amber light bulbs. They shed a soft illumination over the hooked rug at the foot of the steps. The rug was a real antique, he thought—orange sunflowers and yellow roses outlined in black, and black leaves, and the background was like a forest, darkly green. Flowers in a clearing in the wood; he thought: you wouldn't find a rug like that in the department stores. He admired, too, the hat rack that soared up to the ceiling and ended in . . . an eagle on a ball, was it? Or a pigeon on a rosette of flowers? The broad strip of looking-glass down the center of the rack was agreeably clouded—agreeably in that it seemed to point positively to the splendid and durable age of the room's furnishings, of the room itself, of the house that he proposed to buy. Perhaps Miss Loyd would sell him a few of these articles. She wouldn't, for instance, have room for such a big piece of furniture as this rack in an apartment or a small house. It would be pleasant to have a place to store his rubbers. At Mrs. Hlavaty's he had to leave them in the vestibule, and when he put them on in the morning they were like ice: he was sure that half his winter colds came from those rubbers.

In the room at his back, beyond the sliding door, he heard something whirr and flop: the shade going up at the window, he guessed. Then there was a rumbling sound, as of something being moved across the floor. He heard Mrs. Mentone say, "You'd better stay in the parlor for a while," and again there was the imperative "Shhh!"

He thought he had better move. If they found him here it might look as if he'd been eavesdropping. He got up. There was only one place left to sit, the lid of the hat rack cupboard. He lowered himself gingerly, but the seat was hard and narrow, and coats and jackets brushed against his face. He got up again, and so Blanche Loyd found him when she came around through the kitchen. He was hovering uncertainly in the middle of the floor.

"Have you been standing all this time?" she asked, with a flicker of what looked to be amusement.

"Oh, no. I just got up to look—"

She opened the door on the farther side of the staircase. "We'll go in the parlor, if you don't mind," she said. "But I do want you to meet my mother."

She crossed to a table that stood in the middle of the room and pulled the chain on a glass-shaded lamp.

He followed her into the dim room. "I've been admiring your hat rack," he said.

Blanche Loyd laughed. "It isn't much to look at, I admit, but it's handy. An old house never has enough closet space."

"I suppose," he said tentatively, sitting in the chair beside the cold fireplace, which she offered him, and twisting around to watch her as she crossed to the window and drew the shade part way down, "I suppose it will be too big a piece for a smaller place?"

The shade snapped out of her hand and whirred up. Only a moment did she betray herself; then she said, "Oh, dear! We forgot to put out the porch light!"

• 4 •

SENSING, as he could hardly fail to do, her withdrawal from the subject he had thought they would at once settle down to, he said, upon her return from the hall, "I passed a couple of other places with porch lights on and their insides lit up like Christmas trees. That's quite a bit different from my neighborhood."

She smiled. "You should have seen Grant Street a few years ago." She closed the parlor door and crossed rather awkwardly in front of him and sat down on the other side of the fireplace. "Parties," she said; "people coming and going; and at Christmas!—" She looked down. "It's chilly in here, isn't it? I'll light the grate." She got up, took a match from a tubby orange vase that stood on the mantel and, striking it on the bottom of the vase, knelt before him.

He watched the graceful quiverings that her hooped back and shoulders made as she bent forward, bracing herself with one hand, and ran the match along the radiants. In its wake the blue flames leapt out with minute explosions. How old was she? he wondered again. Her skin (the blue flames died away to yellow, red) in the glow of the gas fire (the kitchen match burned slowly down) was smooth and covered by a delicate, transparent fuzz. Peaches and cream, he thought, in the parlance of his youth; and yet she was not precisely either. Her skin was the blanched shade of the wild white rose that had grown in the backyard of his childhood; nor did the delicate warmth in her cheeks bear any resemblance to the ruddy exuberance of the peach. But then, he thought (still she did not rise), all those sayings were a little off: what did it mean, for instance, to describe someone as "brown as a berry"? Berries were red or black or green or blue or white.

With an audible gasp she now jerked backward, flung the match onto the tiles, and blew on the fingers that had held it. "I'll do that once too often," she said, getting slowly to her feet. "And I scold my nephew for playing with matches."

"I hope you didn't burn yourself?"

"No"–she stepped on the expiring flame and kicked the char under the grate–"that is"–she laughed–"just in time! But I've had one of those days: one thing after another. I left a brand-new magazine on the streetcar, and my feet got wet, and at noon I spilled chili on a suit I'd just got back from the cleaners."

"And I came too early."

He waited for a demur, but she replied merely, "I thought that must be your car, but then Mother asked me to help her. It was too bad of us first to keep you shut out, and then to leave you standing in the hall."

"I didn't mind a bit." He added, with quick boldness, "I was glad to have a chance to look around. As I told you, I was admiring . . ." The boldness left him; after her reaction of a moment ago, when the shade flew out of her hand, he could not quite finish the sentence as he had intended. "I was admiring your hallway."

"There's so much waste space in these old houses," she said, resuming her chair (but she looked, he thought, like a bird on a twig, and at any moment he expected her to start off it again). "That partition between the living room and the hall could be pulled down: the living room is far too small. What do people need hallways for any more, anyway?"

"For my purposes," he replied, "an entrance hallway would be very convenient."

"In the old days," she said (she was groping in the pocket of her dress), "it was jammed, piled. At Christmas, with the wreaths at the windows, and red and green bulbs in the lady's hand on the post, and coats! . . . The rack was too small for us then. Galoshes; and people hiding presents under their scarves, and the pretty packages tumbling on the rug, and my brothers' children racing up and down the stairs, and mother coming in and saying, 'What's this? What's *this?*' " (She brought out a handkerchief and regarded it with surprise.) "I thought . . ." (she dug into the pocket again); "do you have a cigarette? I must have left mine in the other room."

He made perfunctory motions, and then he said, "No. I'm sorry. As a matter of fact, I smoke cigars."

"Ah!" She made a wry face. "I remember. . . ." She seemed to grope through a glittering, sliding pile of recollections, each one, he thought, spangled with stars and wrapped round with shining ribbon. "Long ago, at a picnic: they thought I was very 'fast.' " She implied the quotation marks, but whether they were to indicate the antiquity of the expression, or to show her incredulity at its ever having been applied to her, he was not sure. "I took a few puffs. What was almost worse" (here she extracted a bent and wrinkled cigarette from the folds of her handkerchief) "was that it didn't make me ill." She leaned toward him. "But you have a match?"

"Yes. Now, where . . ." He slipped his fingers into his breast pocket. "A lighter," he explained, "but," he added, bringing his hand out, "I changed my suit this morning. I must have left it at home."

"You are temperate," she said. "Then, if you could give me one of the matches on the mantel?"

"Oh, certainly." He got up and took a match from the orange vase and handed it to her.

"Thank you." She struck it against the fireplace tiles and at once expelled the smoke and lifted the handkerchief to her mouth. And was she smiling, he wondered, sitting down.

"I changed my suit," he said. "I must have left it at home."

"I'm sorry I can't offer you a cigar. If Louis Mentone were here . . . but he smokes cigarettes."

"I'm not a great smoker," he said. "At the office we can't, and my landlady doesn't care to have us smoke in our rooms. Too much danger of setting the beds on fire. She likes to have us sit in the living room."

"Very wise," said Miss Loyd absently, "very precautionary. And an ashtray!" she exclaimed. She looked wildly around the room.

"I'll get one," he said, starting to rise (but the depth of the chair occasioned a struggle, and when he had finally got free of it he bumped his thigh against the broad, flat arm. A doily fell to the floor). "Oh, dear!" he cried. "I must have knocked it off." He bent over, the blood rushing into his face, and put the doily back. And where was an ashtray? Amid the cluttered furnishings there must be somewhere a little dish, or a metal shell? He saw bookends made to resemble the façade of a cathedral, more glass-shaded table lamps, a pink candy dish with a top like a pointed roof, a silver letter knife, a plant in a pot, a bouquet of paper flowers.

"Over there," said Miss Loyd, pointing at a long mahogany table." He looked. He saw nothing suitable. "That incense burner," she said, and as he brought it to her she added, "My nephew's—the youngest one. He plays house in here when he comes to stay for a few days with us, but the incense burner is for when he plays church." She took off the metal lid with its square spire, and the ash from her cigarette broke inside. "I can't think where he got the idea. We don't burn anything in our church." She smiled. "My brother Covil worries about him. He's eight, but he still likes to play house, and he goes to bed with four Teddy bears. When he stays here, he sleeps with mother's shawl."

"Well, he'll outgrow it," Mr. Komar said tolerantly.

"I hope not!" she rejoined, emphatically. "He says he never wants to grow up, and I tell him: Keep it off as long as you can. Don't give in to it. Don't hurry to grow up and be young and dull and a nobody. Why are the young today cut all from the same stencil?" she asked. "Look at them!" She swept her arm toward the darker end of the room, the ash from her cigarette spraying onto the rug. "They grow up and become office workers, and they marry into the accounting department, the way one used to marry into the Johnson family or the Armstrongs!"

"It could be a lot worse," he objected.

"Ah!" She crushed her cigarette violently into the squat brass jar. "And they settle into their drab two-family houses, or they buy an ugly bungalow on an ugly street—and who can tell them apart? They live and they die," she said, "and who knows? Who cares? I read about all the Jews who are dying in Europe and I can't feel anything—no pity, no horror. I know it's terrible, but I can't. I only wonder, What did they leave behind? Were they reading a book and did someone come in and say, 'It's time for you to go now,' and did they put down their book and go out, and die? If I could know even that much—just the name of the book they were reading—then I might feel something. But these others, here around us, I know what they're reading: *True Confessions*, *Modern Screen*, and the streetcar slows down, and the conductor shouts something, and they bend a page and close their magazine and go out. I feel for them," she said. "It's worse," she insisted angrily, "it's really worse. Those Jews—they're dying for something; we'll not forget what they've had to do, however little we can feel it—here" (she clasped her breast), "but these little typists: who makes a count of their dying? Sometimes I think the Jew is the only one in this country who has some shred of identification left to him. We can love him, we can hate him, we can protect him (or all three)," she added, smiling, "but we can't forget him. It's poor enough, but what can the rest of us say of ourselves? I am a Methodist, or a Lutheran. I make $26.50 a week. What does that mean?"

"I don't know," he replied.

"That was rhetorical," she said, looking at him amusedly. "But you're quite right: nobody knows. And when I see these little girls with their curly, greasy hair, and these men with their skinny shoulders and their white faces (I pass them every day, at bus stops, in restaurants; they come and buy insurance from me), I think, Poor things!—and then I feel that my heart will break, for I think also, I pity you, I pity you—and I despise you; and what is worse, I forget you. I won't remember when you stop coming, for somebody else, exactly the same, will come and stand in your place. And so I tell my nephew, Do as *you* want. Do as your own self tells you, and when he grows up I'll tell him to pity all the others, who did as they were told, and I'll tell him to hate them, too, for they'll drag him down if they can. It's their last assertion. Trade unions," she said, "I see no danger in them, but I see a terrible danger in the union of thought. All this talk today about there being no islands any more. What does that matter if there are no people to live on them?"

"I don't know!" he protested, for she had stung him. Then he thought he might have played into her hands with that remark. "Things were plenty worse when I was a boy. My father was a good man, I guess, but he couldn't keep a job to save his life. My sister and I went to work just as soon as we were old enough. I got to finish school, but I had a job afternoon and evening the last four years. Sadie was in a bakery by the time she was fifteen. Well, now, all her youngsters are going right through high school, and the oldest girl is at a nurse's school and doing just fine."

"And what do they believe?" she asked.

He thought it a curious question. "What do they believe? Why, we're all Catholics. Sadie's second husband belongs to a Protestant faith, but the little folks have all taken after their mother."

"I see," she said. "And these children—what do they want to do with themselves?"

He laughed, thinking of the manifold and glamorous ambitions that had swept his nephews and nieces. "You know what kids are, always flying from one thing to another. They'll settle down. I was the same way myself."

"You were a romantic?" she asked.

"Romantic? Well, it was silly stuff, if that's what you mean. I wanted to be like that English fellow—you know, Drake?—was that his name? I'd stand on a chair in the front room when Mother was out, pretending it was the prow of my ship, and the parlor table was an island; and I had fights with the cushions. Not very original, I guess."

"And now?"

"You couldn't expect me to be a pirate now? I'm a little stiff to go jumping around stabbing people." He paused and shifted restlessly in his chair. He thought the heat from the fire, after the cold drive, must be making his sinuses ache. "But do you see?" he asked her, leaning forward. His hand slid across the loose doily and gripped its scalloped edge. It seemed to him very important that she understand that he did not think she was right in what she said—not right for everybody, that was; and of course it was embarrassing having her say those things about the Jews. Everybody felt for them these days. He had heard a speech on the radio just the other night, and the man had said that the infamy of the Germans had stained the whole human race, and made a mockery of Christ's suffering on the Cross. "Do you understand me?"

"Yes." She looked him full in the eyes; in the light of the fire her own were dark and luminous, and he could not tell what they expressed. "Yes, I understand. You make me aware of one thing: that it's wrong, morally wrong, to pity anyone."

What a strange response! And how did it fit in at all with what he had wanted her to see? He settled back heavily. He did not know how to answer her; and the doily fell to the floor. ("Oh, *damn!*" he cried in his heart.)

"Would you think me rude if I asked you your first name?" she asked.

"It's Herbert," he said, restoring the doily and pushing the pins viciously into the upholstery. "Hardly anybody calls me that any more except the family."

"Herbert," she repeated. "Herbert Komar. Do you ever say it over to yourself?"

"No. I can't say I do." He smiled, but he felt that it was not altogether a success. "I know what it is."

"You have never said 'I am Herbert Komar'? You've never stood in front of the bathroom mirror and looked at yourself, and felt a terror, as if for that moment some part of you stood off and still managed to see your real self, whole—and stripped: *you?* The something more that your reflection can not show, but that it alone—perhaps—can watch?"

"No. No, I can't say I have. I know who I am."

"Then—who are you? Who is Herbert Komar?"

"Who is he?" he repeated, taking refuge in the third person. "Well, he's a certified public accountant, and—" But still the question embarrassed him. What would Mrs. Hlavaty think if he suddenly went up to her and said, "Who are you?" She'd think he'd lost his mind. He looked at Miss Loyd and could think of nothing to add. He had an insane desire to giggle.

"—And he's Herbert Komar," she finished for him. "Tell me your name."

"Well, now, Miss Loyd, I just told—"

"Surely it can't be hard to say?"

"No," he agreed reluctantly, but he felt a shyness close over him.

"You're not Neville Chamberlain?"

His laughter burst out. Positively, he rocked back and forth in his chair. "No," he said, gasping, "I'm not old man Chamberlain."

"Ah!" she said. She got up. She stood looming above him like that stern other self she had spoken of. "You can tell me who you're *not*."

"And I'm not Tom Mix," he cried—it was the feeblest whisper that emerged. His sinuses were running riot; he could scarcely force the words out of his clogged throat, but still he laughed and choked and rocked in his chair.

"Then—who are you?"

"I'm"—he reached frantically for his handkerchief—"Herbert Komar."

She turned from him, as if she had not got what she wanted and was displeased, and crossed to the window. He heard, as he found his handkerchief and spat into it, the shade roll up, and then she cried in surprise, "It's snowing!" As she came back toward him she said, sadly, "But there's no good in seeing it when you can't do anything about it."

"Yes," he agreed, grateful this time for what seemed another of her swoops and pauses. "When you get older and can't enjoy sledding and making snowballs any more, it's just a nuisance."

Her footsteps broke slightly; they came forward again. "You're right," Blanche Loyd said simply. "I agree. You get too old for the struggle—but," she asked eagerly, "you can still remember?"

"Oh, my, yes. I remember sledding down the hill near our house to the railroad yards. We didn't have a regular sled, but we put a box on runners and waxed them with soap, and it worked very well."

"And now all your boxes have lids on them, and no runners?"

He thought he understood her joke. He chuckled. "That's about it. A box is just a box these days."

"No doubloons in it."

"No doubloons; just old shoes."

"I hope you've got alcohol in your radiator?"

"Well," he said, adjusting himself to the new topic, "I'm all right if it doesn't go below zero. I guess it won't."

"When it snows,"–she came and stood in front of the flaring gas grate, her hands clasped together at the level of her waist– "I feel (this will sound foolish, coming on top of what we've just said), I feel young again, ready to turn over a new leaf." She looked down at him. "Isn't that what you and I are doing tonight, Herbert Komar, in the snow, in the dark: aren't we beginning a new leaf?"

"I hope so," he said simply. "I came here . . ." He paused. After all, he was not now so clear on why he had come. Was it to meet the old Mrs. Loyd, or to talk to Blanche Loyd, or to see, briefly, what the house was like?

She said, taking up the incense burner from the arm of her chair and clapping back its peaky brass roof, "There are five bedrooms, as I told you; only one bath. The pantry back of the kitchen, however: we've often spoken of converting that into a lavatory." She crossed in front of him and put the burner down beside the pink candy bowl. "What plans we've made!" she murmured. Unexpectedly, she chuckled. "Look how it's snowing!"

"It will be a nasty night," he said, thinking of the wet, slippery drive back to Mrs. Hlavaty's, of taking off his rubbers in the cold vestibule; and how he would like to go home to a bath! But it was impossible. He had just had one the night before.

Blanche Loyd cried again, impatiently, "No, no! A beautiful night!" Her hand on the table moved and swept something on its side; he peered into the dark. A snowstorm ball on a teak pedestal lay beside her outstretched fingers. The snow eddied and whirled, pink and lavender and gray in the light of the gas fire. "A new leaf," she repeated, setting the ball upright once more. The bright flakes settled lazily on the little house inside, and on the little fir tree at its door. She bent closer. "It's *cracked!*" she cried. "The glass is cracked!" There was a tragic silence. Then, angrily, she pushed the whirling globe aside. "And now I think I ought to take you to see Mother for a few minutes. She's very anxious to meet you."

"I'd be pleased, I'm sure." He got up, but a paralysis struck his legs. He moved with difficulty around the back of the chair. He cleared his throat. "I understand from your housekeeper that our plan is still . . . that I'm not to say anything about–" (ah! if she would only finish it for him! but she stood there, silent, and as he drew painfully nearer he saw a faint, mirthless smile rimming her lips) "–say anything," he concluded lamely.

"But you'll have to say something," she replied, putting her hand on the knob.

"I only meant," he began miserably, "that naturally I want to spare Mrs. Loyd's feelings about this–matter."

"Say whatever you wish," she replied coldly.

But in the hall she turned to him and put her hand on the sleeve of his coat. Her eyes met his quite frankly, and she said, in hardly more than a whisper, "She is old."

He felt the accusation; he thought he understood the defense that prompted it; and, inexplicably, he felt that he was himself to blame in whatever had transpired between them. He had overstepped.

"The new Plymouths are nice," he said. "I may not get another Chevrolet." (He thought it an inspired subtlety–quite on the required order.) She smiled. He fancied there was a trace of appreciation for his wit in her murmured, "Ah, good."

As she turned once more to lead the way, she said in plainer tones, "We'll have to go around through the kitchen. My mother couldn't bear to be alone upstairs all day, so we made the living room into a bedroom and closed off the entrance through this hallway."

They passed into the dark kitchen. He touched his coat. It felt dry and warm although not much heat was coming up the register. They rounded the doorway into the dining room, which he saw was even more crowded than the parlor. An immense sofa stretched along the nearest wall, and on the further side of the table, in the deep, windowed bay, he saw several upholstered chairs. Just beyond the living room arch, framed by it as if she sat on a tiny stage, was Mrs. Mentone in a cherrywood rocker. She had a horn-rimmed pince-nez clamped on her nose, and she looked, he thought as they approached her through the shadows of the dining room, ineffably distinguished, sitting in the light and the beautiful chair. She was reading a magazine.

"Well, you took your time!" she cried, looking up. She was wiggling her nose at them. The pince-nez popped off, plunged into her lap, and began to climb a silver chain that was flung like a lifeline over her precipitous bosom. The chain ended in a brooch pinned beneath her collar. "You two can take over," she said. She shut her magazine and got up as the glasses completed their ascent. "I'm tired out. I washed the bathroom walls today, Blanche, did I tell you?"

She crossed over to the opposite side of the room. His eyes followed her reluctantly, but with a fascination that had nothing to do with the woman herself. Her movement led him to the chair in which Lily Loyd sat. He sniffed the dry air and felt a little ill with expectation. Could he and Blanche Loyd carry off their deception? For a moment his view of Mrs. Loyd was obscured as Mrs. Mentone leaned across her to shove the magazine into a rack that stood between the old woman's chair and the foot of a metal cot.

Mrs. Mentone straightened up. "I think we're having a nap," she whispered. She stepped back.

Mr. Komar looked full at the old woman. Lily Loyd was short, but enormously heavy. She lay back in her tapestry chair, her yellowish white head, illuminated by the floor lamp beside her, sagging a little sideways against a cushion; her mouth was open, and she breathed with a faint rasping noise. A blanket covered her lap and was wrapped around her legs. She wore a dark blue woolen dress with a white collar pinned at the neck with a large cameo, and she did not look fierce or stubborn; she only looked very old. He found it hard to believe that she could any longer have an attitude toward anything. At her feet the gas grate in the fireplace hypnotically popped, and beyond the front window where Blanche Loyd had stood the boom and fall of traffic went ominously on and on.

They were silent, all of them looking at her. How? he wondered. Were Blanche Loyd and the housekeeper waiting expectantly also? Lily Loyd was withdrawn utterly from their presence: he felt that it was the three waking persons who were captived by the elder brother of death. The sleeper looked to have escaped beyond sleep.

Mrs. Mentone shivered. "Blanche," she said, "I think the furnace is getting low. Does it seem cold in here to you?"

"Open the check."

"I did, about twenty minutes ago, but nothing's happened."

The two women looked at each other solemnly for a moment; Mrs. Mentone suppressed a nervous smile.

"We could wait till Lou gets back. . . ." Miss Loyd began. She looked annoyed, amused.

"Oh, Lord! I'm jumpy enough. I don't want to be cold, too."

"Well," said Miss Loyd resignedly, "I suppose I'll have to go down and look at it."

"I'll bring up the rear. She won't wake up right away."

Miss Loyd turned to him apologetically. "This is an evening of delays," she said. "You understand . . . I think, that is, that I told you about the–the furnace?" He recalled that Mrs. Mentone regarded certain areas of the house as unsafe after the fall of night. Nevertheless, he felt a quick and, he considered, justifiable irritation. If their damned furnace had to be fixed why hadn't they let him wait in the parlor until the job had been done? He thought it was typical female foolishness. Or malice? he wondered suddenly, unreasonably, thinking of the disconcerting talk he had just gone through with Blanche Loyd. But that, he knew, was absurd. Blanche Loyd was—was she not?—on his side; she would not want to antagonize him. Besides, she had known nothing of the state of the furnace until they came in here.

There was a peculiar element of unreality about the whole evening: about that moment in the dark when his glance had met Blanche Loyd's, about the struggle with the front door, as if the house, too, were determined to resist him, about his being led into the presence of Lily Loyd—to find her fast asleep.

Miss Loyd apparently understood his complex reaction, for she said placatingly, "I won't be long. Here. Sit over here. If my mother should wake—of course, she won't—tell her I've just gone down cellar a minute."

"Could I be any help?" he asked hopefully.

"No. Please. Just make yourself comfortable. Have you seen this new *House and Garden?*" She grabbed the magazine off the telephone stand and thrust it into his hands (much as if he, too, were a kind of rack, he thought). "It will give you," she said, "all sorts of ideas," and hurried after Mrs. Mentone. As the two women disappeared into the kitchen, he heard her say, "The furnace! Isn't that the *limit?* Really, Annabelle," she added exasperatedly, and he was certain the remark was meant chiefly for him, "I do think that this once you could have . . . Oh, well." This in resign. And then, more determinedly, "*Some*day I'm going to put in gas."

· 5 ·

HE SAT down almost stealthily in the rocker which Mrs. Mentone had vacated, his hands turning cold in the expectation that Mrs. Loyd might choose now to wake. Between his palms he supported the glossy magazine. He put his knees together and rested his hands with their cradled burden in his lap. Like his seating himself, this was a slow and tentative arrangement. Indeed, he recognized that his whole response to this present involvement was tentative. It was a collective involvement: each statement of Blanche Loyd's, each coping of his own with her remarks, had been an additional accretion. The layers wrapped themselves, dense and murky, around the central issue: the response of the old woman to his presence and his purpose, so that now (this much he saw plainly) the layers would have to be lifted delicately aside, and dealt with each one in turn, before the issue could stand forth clear again. What this laying on had accomplished he was not prepared to say. That something *had* been accomplished–this much he did know. And what on earth was he to say should the old woman wake?

He sat all swathed and muffled up in the light, Mrs. Loyd ignominiously bundled in with him. She resembled, in her billowing contours, he thought, those figure-eight balloons that are sold at fairs, with faces painted on the upper globe and little, useless, cardboard feet attached to the bottom. He lifted his eyes clear of her: he had a conviction that to think about her too long, or to look at her steadily, would be to assure her waking.

(In the depths of the house he heard a shovel slide across concrete, and the lumpy sound of coal falling into it; there was a rattling and clanging, and, inexplicable and eery, the women's laughter.)

On the wall behind Mrs. Loyd was a painting. The light from the floor lamp beside her chair slanted upward across the canvas, so that he could see the eyes of the woman in the portrait, but he could not make out the expression on her mouth, or exactly what it was that she was making with her hands. He had heard many times that in a good portrait the eyes will follow you around the room, and he concluded that, if this were a just criterion, the painting before him was not especially good. The woman's eyes looked away to the right of him, toward the mantel over the angle fireplace. She was sublimely unconscious of her spectator, as unconscious as Mrs. Loyd herself. And were they the same woman? he wondered. It occurred to him that his question was peculiarly phrased: were *they* the same woman —implying still another woman to whom both referred. He tried to see a resemblance between them, but it was difficult with the light blurring the canvas. Each had a high, broad forehead. The brows of the woman in the picture, however, were level and narrow, whereas Mrs. Loyd's—what was left of them—were peaked (even in sleep her face wore an expression of mild astonishment) and shaggy. Still, the eyebrows of the portrait might be a convention. In the shape of their ears he thought he saw a resemblance. Both had long ears, with pendulous lobes, that lay flat against the head. The lady in the portrait wore a jet drop in her left ear (the right he could not see because of the diagonal blur of light), and this both emphasized its length and took away some of its disturbing grossness. Mrs. Loyd's ears were bare, and looked almost obscenely large.

It was, ultimately, the eyes of the woman in the portrait that commanded his greatest attention. They were intensely blue—he was inclined to think it was a blazing blue that only art could have conferred—and their expression was curiously at variance with the formality of the picture: a lady seated in her best clothes, occupied with a little task, against a warm drop of light. Was she laughing? If he could only make out the expression on her mouth. Was she amused, then, and scornful?—it seemed a little; and . . . indulgent? The portrait was not of a quality that would make historical reference unnecessary; it need to be bolstered up with a context. Yet, for all its evident crudity, its second-rate professionality, it had an authority that emanated, he had no doubt, from the lady herself. She was infinitely above, immensely larger than the artist's view, but she had dragged him, gasping, almost up beside her. Yes, one would do that for her—one would gladly try to be as good—the unexpected word quite thrust itself into his mind—as she innocently thought one was. Or *was* that a look of innocence? He could not decide. He did not know how far innocence was corrupted by knowledge, how far purified.

He began very much to hope that this was Lily Loyd. Yet, he felt at once that this lady with the blue eyes was no woman who would balk at the sale of a house. A house would be as quickly cast off as the elegant gown she had probably stepped out of the moment the artist lay down his brush. She was, he thought again, infinitely larger than the poor phenomenal properties that surrounded her. She was indulgent of them, he decided; she even cherished them a little, casually, but she looked beyond them at . . .

The sentence he left unfinished. He did not know what she looked toward. He moved a little, impatiently, in his chair, and brought his flying thoughts back to the living room in Grant Street. For that was not Lily Loyd in that frame; and whatever the blue-eyed lady sought, or had found, was no concern of his. As merely a portrait, a square of canvas and paint, he examined her again. The eyes looked away, looked away. He followed their track. On the mantel, beside a clock with marble pillars and a gilt, pie-crust face, he saw a silver frame with a photograph in it. The light from Lily Loyd's floor lamp slid across the glass, too, and made the subject behind it invisible.

Another member of the family? Or a group photograph. He hesitated before getting up to look, for still Blanche Loyd did not return, and now no sound came up from the basement. He laid the magazine back on the telephone stand and, holding the chair with one hand so it would not rock back as he released his weight, he got up, let the rockers settle quietly under his guidance, and took two steps toward the mantel.

The old woman's hand groped across a doily on her chair arm. She opened her eyes, but she looked not at him, poised above and in front of her, one knee bent in the halfway motion of taking a step; no, she looked around him, beyond him. She was blind. He had forgotten. He remained in the absurd, pantomimic posture, scarcely daring to exhale. Once more, dreadfully, he wanted to laugh.

"Blanche?" inquired the old woman. Her voice was clear and

deep, but it broke a little, making of the name two syllables, the first a statement, the second a half-doubting interrogation. The mantel clock struck nine with a rapidity that suggested it considered its work was done for the night and it was ringing out. At his back, beyond the rocking chair and the telephone stand, he heard snow rustling against the side window. The gas grate sputtered and popped.

The old woman turned her head and looked, he thought, directly at him.

"Who is it?"

He cleared his throat. What could he say? What *could* he say?

"How do you do?" he began. His voice was stuck on some impossible register. Light, unaccented, sexless: no wonder the old woman clutched the doily under her fingers. She might easily have considered that she had awakened to death, and that the voice, with its worldly formality, was actually disembodied.

"Who is it?" she asked again. Her blind eyes held him; they were light and blank, and when the lids flickered down across them it was as if she winked ponderously.

"It's"—he began, with an explosion that briefly cleared his throat—("Tom Mix!" he cried silently; "it's Tom Mix")—"Herbert Komar. I believe Miss Loyd mentioned me to you? She's gone downstairs to fix the furnace. She said to tell you she'd be right back."

"I was having a nap." She added, petulantly, "You were so long!"

"I'm afraid we were. We had to get the—details straight. The insurance . . . I'm sorry I disturbed you. I just got up to—put my magazine back."

"What time was that?" she asked abruptly.

"Nine o'clock."

"I don't think I got your name."

"Komar." He spelled it.

"I am Lily Loyd."

"Oh, I know! Miss Loyd has mentioned you so often."

"Blanche didn't tell me you knew each other well."

"We don't. I meant that she often speaks of you."

"What does she say?"

"What does she say?" (And how were the civilities to be maintained if one's remarks were taken so literally?) "Ah!" he said roguishly. "You might be surprised."

"Won't you sit down, Mr.–Komar, did you say?"

"That's it. Thank you. I believe I will." He went back to the rocker.

"I believe I was asleep when you came in."

"Yes. I hope I didn't wake you."

"Where is Annabelle?"

"Annabelle? Oh! Mrs. Mentone? She went with Miss Loyd."

The old woman chuckled. "And I'd be surprised, would I?"

"I beg pardon?"

"My daughter," she elaborated impatiently. "You think that what she says would surprise me?"

"Oh,"–he laughed and cleared his throat–"yes, I expect it would!"

"And," she said, her eyes fixing on him again, "are you a part of it?"

"A part of it?"

"–Of the surprise."

"I'm afraid you misunderstood me. I meant . . ." But his voice faltered and died. He punctuated the sentence with an apologetic cough.

"I used to know all my daughter's friends," she said musingly. He had the feeling that she was contrasting him unfavorably with the hoards and swarms of people who had once filled the house. "They belonged to the Epworth League, and I saw them at church up the street, and here in the house, too. But of course that old crowd is scattered now, moved away and even quite a few of them dead. Now I rarely know where she goes, whom she sees. Have you lived in the city all your life?"

"Yes. I was born here, down on old Lark Street. Do you know where that is?"

"Is it on the west side?"

"No; it's the near south side—though when we moved there it was almost the end of the line."

"The south side," she murmured, and now her disapprobation of him was unmistakable. "Factories?" she asked. "Factories and foreigners?"

"I suppose you might think of it that way," he agreed reluctantly. He remembered Blanche Loyd's identification of the south side in her office Friday afternoon. Had the old woman now completed the phrase over which the daughter had hesitated and at last left broken off?

"I wonder if you would mind getting a pillow off my daughter's cot and slipping it behind me? I can't seem to get straight."

He got up, took one of the sofa pillows heaped along the foot of the cot, and slipped it behind her. She pulled herself up, with a difficulty that he found touching despite his resentment.

"I hope you don't think I meant anything personal," she said, when he was seated again. "I haven't been over that way in years—not since one of my sons rented a house there soon after his marriage. But I was a little put off. The narrow streets—in some of them it was almost impossible for two cars to pass without scraping. And the crowds! And the little stores: I felt sure they were all smelly inside, and dirty. And the houses jammed up together and practically on the curb. Of course," she added sadly, "look at us. But Grant Street was not this way twenty years ago. And the dirt!" she exclaimed. "Factory chimneys shooting up all round one, and railway tracks in people's backyards."

"Yes," he said, "it was that way; still is. But," he went on defensively, "you didn't see it up close enough."

"I suppose it's just what you get used to."

He nodded, forgetting with her gaze still on him that she could not see his assent.

"Were your parents born here?" she asked presently.

"My mother was. My father came from the old country. He was"—he remembered his father, and he brought it out heavily—"he was very disappointed. If it hadn't been for my mother, I think he might have gone back. But Momma didn't want to go someplace where she thought everybody talked an outlandish gibberish. Her own people came from Europe, but she wouldn't speak a word of the language. She had a very fine delivery, and when we were young she used to give us elocution lessons—you know, talking with a match burning in front of your mouth? Things like that. She selected treasures of English literature and made us read them aloud, and when we blew out the match she made us start over again. I recall I never could say Bulwer-Lytton without that match going right out."

He thought she had not heard him. Her fingers opened and closed spasmodically on the arm of her chair, and her jaw moved ever so slightly up and down. As he watched, he saw her tongue flicker out and run along her lips. Her eyes were closed now.

"Well," he said finally, "it's going to be a nasty night." He half swung round in the rocker, and let it fall slowly back so that he could look through the window. But with the lights on the panes the outside was merely black and shining, and he could see no more than the snow mounting along the window sill.

"The Loyds," said the old woman, "have been in America three hundred years."

"That's certainly a long time!" he exclaimed, with an enthusiasm that was largely the result of having the silence broken.

"It can hardly be measured in time—what a stay like that means," she replied.

"No. I suppose it wouldn't seem much to English people."

"But for most of it," she said, "they've been in Canada. Blanche and the boys are citizens here, however. I am not."

"I guess you feel about the way my father did. He never became a citizen either."

Mrs. Loyd's jawline suddenly grew rigid. "A little bit different," she said. "I'll be buried back where I belong—on a hill near my husband's old home. He and I bought our plots years ago, though we didn't know then that he'd be in his so soon."

"I have a nice plot out in Luray Memorial Cemetery," he said. "Just before she died I bought my mother a plot there, too. She was really surprised. Poppa was buried close in town, but they dug that cemetery up to make room for the streetcar barns, so we put him out beside Momma. I'm sorry he never lived to see it. It's a beautiful place. No monuments, you know: little tablets, instead. And on Sundays they have an organ concert at the mausoleum."

"Our cemetery isn't like that," she said.

He did not know if she spoke by way of boast or disclaimer.

"It's a shaggy one," she continued; "the tombstones are of all sorts, and some so old no one knows any longer who's under them."

"I like an old cemetery, too," he protested. "But you have to be careful in the city, you know. I'll tell you that one experience with my father taught all of us a lesson."

"I have no roots in this country," said Mrs. Loyd. "My own people came from England right to Ontario. Blanche and my sons all feel that this is native ground, since the Loyds settled first on Manhattan."

"Is that a painting of you, up there on the wall?"

"Behind me? No, that's Mary Bush, my husband's stepmother—though Mary was younger than he was."

"I guess she was a beautiful woman?"

"Not by the standards of that day. She was fresh-faced, but so was everyone else. She was too thin and small to be a beauty when she came, and later on she lost her figure altogether. And I always thought her eyes bulged a little. She was Irish. You know how prominent their eyes are?"

"The eyes look lovely in the picture—so blue."

"Oh, she'd be a beauty by your standards, but she wasn't much admired in Yarmouth. My father-in-law met her not long after she got off the boat from Ireland. His first wife had died. I forget now what he was doing up in Nova Scotia, but anyway he brought her back with him."

"Was she very young?"

"Old enough to make trouble, I'll vouch for that. He married her for her own salvation, he'd say years later. She came of a good Cork family—good as the Irish go, I mean. They had her in a convent, and one night she got her things together and slipped away. That was in the seventies some time. She came to America with a man and woman she hardly knew, though she insisted they were second cousins. Well, they turned out a raffish pair, and it was her good luck she ran into Jeremiah Loyd."

"Was she happy?"

"As anyone, I suppose. She was ailing, though: she died before she was forty."

"Mary Bush," he repeated, looking at her brilliant, elusive eyes.

"She was a Catholic," said Lily Loyd. "Converted, of course: my father-in-law held strong views on that subject. But she was always partly an outsider. We used to tell her she'd have a hard pull through Purgatory. Oh!" she laughed, "what a temper she had!" She paused and shifted, and the pillow at her back slipped up and pushed at her neck so that for a moment she looked like a malevolent turtle. "She drew the men," she said. She moved again; the pillow fell on the floor.

Mr. Komar did not move from his chair.

"My father-in-law used to say it wasn't safe to leave her alone for a minute. Not that she meant anything by it, but the Irish don't see things the way we do. She had that painting made when a group of us were away in Toronto for a week. She *said* the man didn't even charge her for it! I ask you! But the house was full of people the whole time, and, anyway, she's dead and gone now." She chuckled. "*And* forgotten. He never would hang the picture. He wrapped it in a quilt and left it in the attic."

"Left what in the attic?" asked Blanche Loyd, coming into the room. Mr. Komar got up. "No, no, sit still. Well, I see you've met. I'm sorry I was so long." She held up two spotless palms. "We had to break a couple of lumps to get them in. I was *filthy*."

Mr. Komar said, "Mrs. Loyd has been telling me about the lady in the painting."

"Grandma Loyd? Wasn't she lovely? Though when I remember her she didn't look a bit like that. She was middle-aged, and she'd gotten heavy. Mother's rather like what she'd have been if she'd lived."

There was, on Mr. Komar's part, an anguished and yet delighted pause, and on the part of Mrs. Loyd, he judged, an outraged withdrawal from the whole subject.

"Is it any warmer in here?" Blanche Loyd asked.

"I don't see why you let that furnace go so long, Blanche," said her mother. "All this fuss about the basement."

"Now, mother, you know you're always telling me we let it get too hot," said Miss Loyd placatingly.

"I went up and down those steps for years, and I didn't make any hue and cry about it," said her mother implacably.

"Nor do I, I'll remind you. But you ought to know how Annabelle is. Did you have a nice nap?"

"No. I didn't. I was cold, and I dreamed that—"

"Well, it has got colder. It's snowing, you know. Did Mr. Komar tell you it was snowing?"

"Who?"

Miss Loyd looked anguished. "Mr. *Komar*."

"Is that—"

"Yes, mother, it is."

"No, he didn't. Or if he did I don't remember. He's been telling me about his *life*. He was born right here in the city, on the *south* side."

"But he doesn't intend to spend the rest of his life on the south side," said the victim of this exchange, with a rashness that sprang from Mrs. Loyd's dismissal of him.

"Mr. Komar is looking for a house to buy, Mother," said Miss Loyd. She crossed nervously to the cot and sat down.

In the following silence the twang of the metal lacing on the cot was distinctly audible. The clock on the mantel announced the quarter hour.

"What time is that?" asked Mrs. Loyd.

"Nine-fifteen," said her daughter.

"Do you have a long drive, Mr. Komar?"

Mr. Komar moved as if to rise, but Blanche Loyd shook her head at him furiously, and he subsided. "Yes," he admitted, "pretty far."

The old woman shut her lips tightly, folded her hands in her lap, and closed her eyes again.

"What sort of house do you have in mind, Mr. Komar?" Blanche Loyd asked with light, unconvincing interest.

"Why, I want to find a big place that has a lot of extra rooms. I thought of keeping the first floor for myself, and renting the upstairs rooms to students at the university."

"There are plenty of big houses on the market," announced Mrs. Loyd.

"Yes. I don't suppose I'll have any trouble."

"Today," she continued (it was like listening to a loudspeaker), "people want these little houses with no dining room, and no pantry, and they squeeze themselves somehow into two bedrooms."

"I guess that's right. I never know how my sister's family manages to fit into their place."

"It's not quite as easy as you make it out, Mother," said Miss Loyd. "Mr. Komar can't be too far from the university, and he has to be near the bus or the streetcar lines."

"He'll have no trouble." The old woman grunted. "Tell him to look along Grant Street. It has its share of fools."

Mr. Komar got up. "I've got quite a drive in front of me. This has been very enjoyable. Goodnight, Mrs. Loyd."

She made not even the formal protest at his going. "Goodnight. I hope you find your house." Her eyelids flickered up, and, as she gave him her old hand, she actually grinned at him. "Try Grant Street," she repeated.

He looked at her; he felt the muscles going hard in his cheeks. There was no doubt in his mind that she saw his discomfiture. "I shall," he told her.

"Good. I am sorry we won't meet again, Mr. Komar. I always enjoy talking to my daughter's—clients, and hearing what she says about me. But I am afraid you have not surprised me as much as I had hoped."

· 6 ·

"I'M GLAD you could come, Mr. Komar, and sorry I left you stranded with Mother that way."

They stood in the dark kitchen; he was slipping into his coat. "*That* feels good," he said, "but the heat won't last. It was kind of you to have me over."

"I think . . ." There was, again, the suggestion of restrained mirth. "You've been kind, too." He felt her eyes merciless on his face. "I hope you've got to know us?"

In what seemed to him her arrogance she made of it a half statement. He was grateful that her words came out while he was buttoning his coat, for the small business prevented his having to look at her; but presently, when the buttons were undeniably in place, when he had found his gloves and turned up the collar on his coat, he was obliged once more to lift his eyes. He was seized with a tired, helpless anger and a burrowing humiliation.

Had she really intended this confident interrogation as—as it seemed to him—a final thrust, a last turning of the blade? He saw that she was not even aware of his response. Her hands played idly with two soft, woolly pompoms that hung down from the throat of her blouse; her face was turned away. He noted the profile. In the dark it was the fulness of that profile that betrayed—and by no means completely—her aging. Out of his humiliation and the fatigue from which either it issued or it was consequent upon, he was able to construct a kind of irrationale of what-might-have-beens that in their larger applications caught up this night's experience into, as it seemed to him then, his total experience. Blanche Loyd might almost have been a girl saying goodnight to her beau. And "beau" he must call himself. He might, in the half-light of his conflicting emotions, be able to visualize both himself and her as young again, but he could not so far transcend time as to make them young in this present instance. He was, then, like a beau, and the time—it was any time except now. They might, he reflected, this younger Herbert Komar and this gentler Blanche Loyd, have paused here for their brief understanding after an especially bad evening with the old people in the parlor. And it was not that he condemned her for the exactions of her family: it was her complicity in their stand that he found so disappointing and baffling. But he was tired enough, too, to admit even to himself (and admission was surely the last extremity and lucidity of fatigue?) that he had been a willing apprentice to their art.

"I remember . . ." Blanche Loyd began. Her eyes glanced across him, and then away. He followed, this time, her absorbed gaze. Beyond the kitchen windows the night was brilliant and restless. The undulant clouding of steam across the panes partly veiled the light and movement, made them more provocative and impelling. Snow slid, plopped, stuck against the sills. He saw a tree near the drive thrash its limbs and shake a gray cloud onto the ground.

"Years ago," she said, beginning again; "my mother never thought much of the beaux I brought home."

He was lifted briefly out of his humiliation and tiredness. Once more they were trembling on the edge of a mutual clarity.

"His name . . . what was it? It doesn't matter. He spent a miserable evening!" She threw back her head and laughed. "Mother frightened him to death!"

He found it impossible to respond, though he felt his imminent peril. On what she said next: there lay the plank, or the abyss.

She moved restlessly from his side. At one of the windows she bent over and ran her hand across its lower pane.

"Do you know what I told him?" she asked, looking out.

He saw her breath steam up again the clearing she had made. He still could not trust his voice. He shook his head.

She whirled around. "What did I tell him?" she demanded.

He remained mute.

"I told him," she said exultantly, "You've got to fight it! That's the way. That's the meaning!"

"And–" he managed to bring out.

Her shoulders slumped. "I've forgotten his name," she said quietly.

It was not possible for him to misunderstand, but he did not know whether in fact she had laid down the plank for him to cross, or hurled him precipitately over the edge.

"I left my rubbers in the hall," he now said.

She moved obediently forward, and when they reached the front of the house she lifted the rubbers off the register and handed them to him. "Watch out. They're hot."

He took them and sat down in the chair before the sliding door. It was eery to think of the old woman, silent and victorious, sitting on the other side of that door in her tapestry chair; sitting almost at his back; for he had come, it seemed, a great way since their defiant parting. He did not feel anger now, or even especially humiliation. He felt merely his tiredness; after all, he was not a young man, and when you work hard all day from eight-thirty until five, and emerge to face this . . . he thought he would be glad to leave this house and never to see it again.

"I wonder," he began, drawing on the second rubber and wiping his hands on his gloves, "how much of the world's work fails for no better reason than that people get tired?"

She looked at him with the alert, sympathetic gaze that Mrs. Hlavaty assumed when he began to speak circumspectly about the lack of hot water; he had come to recognize the expression as the invariable prelude to an automatic response. It was like his own getting up when a lady entered the room: a convention with no real meaning left behind it. Ladies with alert expressions, gentlemen perpetually rising and shaking their newspapers loose: there was the commotion of life for you. All this hopping up and adopting attitudes one could never feel: no wonder people wore themselves out. And so his brief excursus brought him back to what he had intended to say, though now he addressed not Blanche Loyd but himself, the self she had described as the watcher in the bathroom glass.

"I mean," he said, "what's behind all our mistakes and our failings? Why is nothing that we do ever as good as it might be? Are we too stupid to do better, or are we afraid? I don't know. I don't hold so much with ideas about fate. I think," he went on, aware of the anticlimax, and of expressing not fully enough what he meant, what he thought he understood, "I think people get tired out. All of us have just so much energy to get through life with—I'm very superstitious about this—and when we've used it up there's no getting a second supply. If we burn it all away when we're young, trying for what we think we want, then everything's *got* to go well with us later on, for if we're balked there's no fighting it. I don't know if you can hoard it, either. It's like dry cleaner: if you don't use it when it's fresh it evaporates, and even what's left is pretty weak stuff. Old age," he went on, "is like that, isn't it? A half-empty bottle of cleaner. You have to scrub mighty hard to get the spots off—and maybe the scrubbing isn't worth it, because by the time you've got everything clean the bottle is empty." He got up and put on his hat. "I'll be getting along."

As she took his hand, she smiled into his face. Her eyes moved; he saw her take in the gray frizzle of hair beside his ears, his brown eyes behind the rimless glasses, his trembling mouth.

"Goodbye?"

Ah! he knew it. The bright, deceptive glance. ("Why, I don't *doubt* you, Mr. Komar; but isn't it strange that everyone else seems to get enough hot water?") He chose to ignore the interrogation, as, he recognized in his tired lucidity, he had all his life ignored leading questions.

She opened the door. (It flew out effortlessly, he noticed.) He stepped past her and pushed at the storm door. The porch was drifted with snow, and beyond the roof the flakes fell with a steady hiss.

"The streets will be bad," she said. "Drive carefully. Shall I put on the light?"

"No, thank you. I can see my way down." He turned and looked at her sadly. "You'd better get in out of the cold."

"I will. Goodnight. Watch your footing on those steps. Someday,"—she hesitated—"someday, someone will have to get them fixed."

He crossed the porch, his rubbers gritting on the snow, and started down the steps.

"Goodnight," he said; and was it a promise? He did not know.

As she closed the door she called something to him. He could not quite get it. "Goodnight"? Had she only repeated that? Or had she flung the imperative "Fight!" at him? He wouldn't put it past her, and he did not care.

The car was cold. The engine revolved, caught, and died again. When he had finally got it going, he sat there several minutes longer, letting the motor warm. He looked at the house. The hallway light had been extinguished. The upstairs was dark. In the old woman's room the shade was once more across the window.

The house had withdrawn into its labyrinthine self. He felt isolate; he felt that it had forgotten him; that, worse, he had passed through it without once impressing upon it the fact of himself.

He looked up through the lacings of wet branches. Snow beat incessantly at the wooden walls, but, striking, the flakes cascaded down in routed heaps, melting into the gutters along the porch roof. Attack and rout. Under some future sun the last flakes would succumb, and hardy and glittering the house would burst out into the light. People would climb the steps; the door would open and close; in the old woman's room Mary Bush would still be engaged with whatever perpetual task occupied her hands, and her eyes—so blue—would look across the corner of the room . . . at what? He had never seen what was in the silver frame. The old woman herself: there she would sit, too, triumphant and crippled, and someday, perhaps (it was the greatest recognition he could hope for), she would say to her daughter:

"Who was that man?—you know, he came the night we had our first snow."

And Blanche Loyd would laugh. "How you frightened him! I don't know. I've forgotten his name."

PART THREE

The Interior People

· 7 ·

"Then we can consider it settled?"

Herbert Komar sat back in the uncomfortable wooden chair and tried to ignore his feeling of incredulity. To admit it, as he would rather have wished to do (was this not victory?), would have been to admit also that he had given over expecting to get the house, that this luncheon with Blanche Loyd had been intended as a gesture, a defiant last forcing of himself on the indifferent household in Grant Street.

So occupied was he with the fine adjustment which he required of his response that he did not notice his companion's silence.

"I don't know," he continued, "exactly why I should sound surprised. I suppose I didn't expect your mother to give in." He smiled at Blanche Loyd openly (he could afford now, he told himself, this tolerance). "I'd about decided I'd have to try somewhere else along Grant. She . . . I thought Mrs. Loyd seemed a little"—but the bruise was not so soon eased, and he rummaged for a word that would express not quite what he meant—"of course," he picked up falteringly, "I couldn't blame her for feeling resentful of me." Yes, "resentful" was a happier choice than "scornful," or "amused." He murmured, "All those years!" The wonderment was less at Lily Loyd's surrender than at his winning. "Well, now," he said briskly, "this calls for a celebration. How about another pot of tea? And I'll have more coffee, too."

With his napkin he brought down a fluttering waitress and gave her their orders. The napkin had often been flung out thus in the past, and usually had billowed earthward without its prey, for the help in cafeterias knew it was there to clear off tables, not to fill the capricious extra requirements of the diners. It seemed to Mr. Komar that the success of his gesture today was propitious. He had noticed before how, when everything was going well, all the small details of life seemed for a time to operate smoothly.

"I can't tell you," he resumed, "how pleased I am. . . ." Indeed, he reflected, this was the truth: he really could *not* tell her. One cannot pay personal tribute to oneself; at least, not without being vulgar.

The waitress returned with their coffee and tea. "The service here is very good," said Miss Loyd when the girl had left again. "But of course I don't suppose she has much to do now"—and, indeed, the vast cafeteria on the second floor of the building in Third Street was almost empty. It was past two on a rainswept Friday afternoon. They had known each other just a week.

The waitress returned with an empty tray and began to collect and stack their plates and sauce dishes. She bore these away to another table, but before Mr. Komar could open up the important subject again she was back with a damp rag. With a degree of care that he, with growing impatience, thought he had never observed before in any cafeteria employee, she wiped around Miss Loyd's teapot and saucer, his own cup, and the plate with the half-eaten slice of Boston cream pie slowly dying on it.

"How cold it's been!" remarked Miss Loyd.

"Yes. I . . ."

"*Much* colder," Miss Loyd affirmed. "I think the weather changed the very night you came to see us. Wasn't it on Monday that it began to snow?"

The waitress now removed their bowl of sugar and substituted another, fuller bowl.

"Thank you, miss."

He spoke with what he hoped was finality. It was provoking that a simple request for more tea and coffee had brought all this on them. As the waitress emptied their ashtray into a dirty saucer, he lifted his coffee cup and said, determining to ignore the girl no matter how long she persisted in ministering to them, "Well. Well . . . happy landings!" Or did that sound very lame? "Here's to . . . here's to success!" he added.

"Oh, dear!" cried Miss Loyd. "Lemon! No, no, that's all right"—this to the waitress—"I didn't tell you, did I? Never mind. I think I have enough cream left from before."

Defeated by this small flurry, Mr. Komar put down his coffee. A cafeteria was hardly the place for a toast, anyway, nor were coffee and tea appropriate beverages. Perhaps, too, a good toast needed to be drunk in a crowd, amid incessant, complicated noise, if it was to seem momentous. Around them the empty tables sat square and desolate; they had not even cloths to soften their hard outlines, or silver to brighten them, or lamps to shut out the rainy afternoon twilight. A kitchen boy with a broom and dustpan moved among them, and the counterpointing that Mr. Komar felt the celebration required was supplied only by the monotone of city traffic, diminished in the slide of rain, and by the small clatter that the boy's pan made against the linoleum floor. Mr. Komar faced toward the wide, thick-paned front windows of the cafeteria. The buildings on the farther side of the narrow street seemed pasted against them by the runny glue of rain, for they were as dimensionless as the occasion itself. Music schools, modeling schools, chiropodists' and chiropractors' offices, reducing salons, costume jewelers: the neighborhood dumbly resisted celebration.

No, an occasion was made impossible; he regretted that he had not braved the celebrity of a restaurant in one of the main thoroughfares. He had eaten lunch in Makio's Cafeteria for several years:—there was the trouble, for he had the urban worker's occupational dread of venturing off the tried territory.

Mercifully, having lavished on them a pair of well-filled salt and pepper shakers and a full container of paper napkins, the waitress withdrew.

"We'll drink a real toast another time," he said to Blanche Loyd, and to himself he promised her linen napkins, a hostess in black, a table with a cloth, flowers, mirrors, carpeting on the floor. The propriety of bringing a lady to a cafeteria: he saw, too late, that there was none.

Blanche Loyd looked at him soberly. "You make it so hard for me to go on," she said.

He saw real distress in her face, and instantly his mood swung about. He was overcome by another kind of thoughtlessness, by his wish to celebrate what to her might be defeat—or at best expediency.

"I'm sorry," he said quickly. "I forgot that it was your home. I was so pleased. . . ."

He did not go on; it was impossible to suppress his jubilance. He looked away from the pain in her eyes; now, how thankful he was for the emptiness of the room, the utilitarian surroundings. In the silence and the isolation she would be able to compose herself.

"I am ashamed," she said presently.

He looked at her in astonishment. "*You?*"

"Mr. Komar, I didn't . . . you didn't let me finish my story."

He asked bewilderedly, "What more was there to tell? If your mother has agreed to sell, the big problem is settled, isn't it? Please," he said, leaning forward, wanting to make amends for what he had not done, for the too much he had wished to do, "please don't think that I won't give you as much time as you need. Is that the trouble? There's no hurry. I know you'll want to look around a bit so that what you get will really suit you."

"Oh . . . wait!" she said urgently. "You go too fast!"

He was silent. Then, "Is the price too low?"

"This has nothing to do with the price. It's"—she stopped and fumbled in her handbag. She lifted out a handkerchief and put it on the table, and a green leather keycase, her whole concentration bent, it seemed, on her search. With her head still lowered, she said, "You were quite right to think that the matter was settled. As I told you, Mother agreed with all the arguments I brought up. The house is hers, but of course I am the one who keeps it going, and it's largely my money that pays the mortgage. She agreed that the final decision would have to be mine. As in the past, she was quite"—Miss Loyd brought out a cigarette and, as she raised it toward her lips, raised her eyes briefly—"sympathetic. Of course she had guessed what you came for. I knew she would. Our pretense"—she thrust the keycase and handkerchief back into her purse and snapped it shut—"was not intended to deceive her."

He must have looked his shock. Had they been engaged that night in an elaborate deception that had no point—no point at all, since they were all principals who knew how the play came out, none of them spectators? What a pleasure she took in humiliating him!

"I hope you're not angry?"

"I'm surprised," he answered shortly. "Your mother played her part well."

"No, no! You misunderstand me. She knew nothing about you, before you came, except that you wanted to talk to me about an insurance policy. But she could hardly have helped guessing your real purpose. What I didn't make clear to you before is the fact that we have almost no visitors who are not members of the family or else friends whom we've known for years. I do very little business at home, and since Mother's been ill I've always taken strangers into the parlor. My mother rarely meets them. Naturally, when I told her about you, and told her I wanted you to meet her, she suspected that you were more than . . . well, that you were not simply a client, or not the client I had made you out to be."

"Then why," he asked stiffly, "did we make any effort to keep my real business from her?"

She looked at him helplessly. "It was a sort of buffer," she answered. "Less painful, both for her and for myself, done that way. If I had gone to her and said that in you we had a buyer, she would never have agreed to see you—or if I had made her agree she would suddenly have got ill—had a stroke . . . oh, *any*thing," she said. "She's wonderful that way! Her resources are endless, and her cunning . . ." She broke off. "Your coming opened up avenues—ways of persuading her that would never have been possible had you been simply a name." Abruptly, she said, "You've changed your suit today."

"Why," he agreed, "yes, I have."

"And come away without your lighter!" she exclaimed sadly.

"My lighter?" He frowned. "I have it right here. Oh!" He paused, embarrassed. "I'm sorry. Here, let me give you a light." As he snapped the chromium lever in front of the cigarette she was holding, he remembered that earlier exchange in the parlor in Grant Street, when he had handed her the match from the orange vase, and she had covered her face in quick—amusement, had it been? "You have a long memory, Miss Loyd." He knew that he had flushed, and his humiliation died entirely in his anger.

She looked at him across the pale flame. "An attention to detail can be valuable, Mr. Komar."

He drew back. "That's above my head," he replied. He noted that his voice neither diminished in volume nor shook. "In fact, all this is pretty much over my head. Has Mrs. Loyd agreed to sell," he went on quickly, "or hasn't she?"

"She agreed at once." Blanche Loyd's eyes met his with a splendid candor. There was no shading in them, he saw, nor any depth. "As usual, but more—more fervently," she said, flicking ash into her saucer. "That was what troubled me."

"It couldn't be that she knew you were right," he said with a heavy sarcasm, "and that she was sick of fighting, tired of her own strategies and yours, as well?" He paused as a new idea struck him. "I suppose it really is your *mother* who doesn't want to sell?"

"My mother," said Blanche Loyd evasively, "has never been tired in her life. Agreement was her strategy, as your posing as a client was mine—mine and yours," she amended. "Nothing was really concealed on either occasion." She sighed, and for the first time she looked, he thought, like a woman who was past middle age. The hard electric glare in the room robbed her soft skin of its delicate color, and its gentle collapsing over the bones of her face gave him the sensation that a mask had slipped, just slightly, but that the next years would see an increasing displacement and a final surrender to the fleshy blur of old age.

"Then—she hasn't agreed at all," he said finally; and he, too, felt old, and had one of those rare, fleeting recognitions of the fact that he would grow even older, old as Lily Loyd herself, if he lived that long. He marveled, even in his dismay, at her energy, and his anger, in its turn, died before this hard glimpse of mortality.

"She said one thing," Miss Loyd murmured, crushing out her cigarette; "she said, 'Well, that will be the end of us.' " She looked away from him, across the room at the slight, springy form of the kitchen boy. "And there's the crux of it." She added, with a quick fierceness, "She's right, Herbert Komar. She's looked squarely at what I was afraid to look at. She's *proud*," she herself said proudly.

He wondered if she had not answered his earlier question, but in his rejoinder he kept to the problem as Blanche Loyd had laid it out. "She's right not to sell a house that is bleeding the life away from you? She's right to keep you tied to a thing that's made of plaster and wood? She's *wrong!*" he said vigorously. "But she's proud. I'll grant you that."

And he thought suddenly of Mary Bush, who belonged to that other house in Canada, but belonged also, through the Loyds, to the house in Grant Street. Her image was very plain in his mind. He knew what she would have done. She would have laughed, and flung her arms out to the sky. She would have known the real rightness, and it would have had no connection with a house. But she was dead, dead and nailed flat in that shaggy graveyard where Lily Loyd would someday lie. He felt the familiar, paralyzing tiredness.

"Right and wrong," he said. "Houses are bought and sold every day, and people's morals don't seem any the worse."

"I know. I know why you think her wrong, too. But when we go, that will be the end of us. She is right to see that."

"*How* will it be the end? Why need anything be changed, except for the better?"

"We will have surrendered."

"You said that once before, I remember. Do you mean to me? Is that how you think of me–as an invader?"

"We will have surrendered to . . . well, as I told you, to the way things are. We will be like all the other people in the city, tenants in boxes. Has it never struck you how life today is made up of windowless rooms? The room of living, the room of business, the room of pleasure, the room for dying–and they are scarcely distinguishable. The walls are all the same, all narrow and low, and the furnishings look alike, and the people: there's the tragedy, for one can not distinguish among them, either. They are the eager prisoners of the stone house. Its streets are their corridors, and endlessly they walk back and forth along them, turning into one room, into another. If they go away or die it hardly matters, for the crowds at the door are waiting to push in and fill up the space they have left; and who will notice they have gone? Listen!" she commanded fiercely. "Hear them!"

And far away, in the streets, on the bridges, from the ground, the air, he heard the faint hoots and roarings; he thought, too, that he heard feet trampling ten thousand pavements, heard doors swing in and elevators buzz up, buzz down.

Once again, as on Monday evening in the dark parlor in Grant Street, he felt himself roughly dislodged from his position as the equable and certain man who accepted without rebellion the domination of the divine, impersonal brush. Blanche Loyd's was, certainly, not an uncommon view of urban life; he had heard it, read it, a hundred times before, and she was herself only extending those remarks that she had made there in the parlor. But he recognized that the bedlam she denounced was not only an urban one. The metaphor of a howling, dingy, interior people extended, in her view, to all life: thus her anger, her passionate cynicism. And he was, to the Loyds, one of this anonymous, self-destructive mob, briefly singled out because he was a threat to them: he might, if they capitulated to him, suck them in, too. The daughter felt this as vividly as the mother, though in the question of the house she appeared compelled to his side. He suspected bitterly and perhaps unfairly that the Loyds would have welcomed any kind of scoundrel or windy aggressive fool: anyone who positively felt and made himself felt by others, agreeably or not. He thought it an irony that their vision of life should be so much what his own was, that only the angle they saw it at should be different.

He looked at Blanche Loyd. She stared beyond him into the shabby depths of the undistinguished restaurant, and he knew that there was in his vision of life no room for celebration, so that, in bringing her here, he had unconsciously affirmed his opposition to everything that the Loyds believed. He knew further that moments earlier, when he had regretted his choice of a place to eat, and just now when he had thought of Mary Bush—after all, *their* Mary Bush—he had in fact damned his opposition, gone, however innocently, over to their side. Yes, he betrayed himself as much as he was betrayed by the Loyds; and recognizing this he thought once more of Monday night, but this time it was of that part of the evening after he had driven away from Grant Street, through the snow and wind, across the ugly urban miles to his room on the south side. He had gone directly upstairs. The house was quiet, everyone either asleep or reading in bed. He had gone to the bathroom and looked at himself in the looking glass let in the door of the medicine chest, and fear had slackened his wrists and calves so that he had, as he leaned forward, gripped the cold porcelain of the washbowl until the joints in his thin fingers ached. He had intended, alone in the tiled room, to assure his image that he knew it was there. But, "I am—"; only that much had be brought out. To say that he was himself, that he was Herbert Komar: he could not. The irrepressible laughter had sprung dreadfully to his throat. He had watched in horror and panic as the reflected mouth quivered, and then he had turned quickly away and gathered up his towel and washrag, lest he let that other self see his profound mirth at the fact of their being someone called Herbert Komar.

He had in his life regretted very rarely that he was alone; indeed, those crowded years in Lark Street being always present in his mind, he had often rejoiced in his freedom. But in that moment of turning away from the glass he had felt not only alone and intolerably lonely, but sealed off. What had he missed? He did not know. He wondered if the other dwellers in this endless house of stone had, in their various ways, all missed it too? He wondered what happened to them when they were shut away into their separate cubicles. Had they any private, affirming consciousness? If he were, some midnight, to fling open Miss Kasco's bedroom door, would he find emptiness beyond it, and the lingering scent of gardenia?

He thought wryly that his was the area which must, in principle, stand against conviction, unable even to defend the principle of non-conviction. And he recognized that ultimately it was his own ambivalence toward what he believed—toward the absolute law of the brush—that made him go on irresolutely pursuing the Loyds, even after today's humiliation and the humiliations of Monday night.

Blanche Loyd, aware of his gaze, now fixed her cold, beautiful eyes on him. He wet his lips and groped for something positive to say. But still he only looked at her in a kind of sad horror. He forced himself at last to say, "It wouldn't be the end of you—leaving that house." Look at me! he wanted to cry, and was aware that she did just that. And did she take his look as a plea for the reassurance he could not give himself? He could not guess; he could not even guess what he would have meant by it himself had he so commanded her. "You'd go on just the same," he added resolutely.

Her agreement, with those hard eyes on him, was almost sinister. "We would go on." Her lids dropped; she looked abruptly tired. She added, after a pause, "We will have to go on."

This time he jumped to no conclusions. "Does that mean . . ."

She shook her head impatiently. "It means–nothing. Or everything. It means what you want it to mean."

"What if I asked you point-blank? What if I said: Is this house for sale? What would you tell me?"

"I would tell you–no."

"But if I asked no question?"

"Then you would not make me give an answer."

He pulled himself erect in the chair. "That's straight enough," he said, and he meant it literally; nor was it till later that he saw his words as a touchstone by which he could gauge how far he had left behind the uncomplicated and unquestioning man who had, on a Friday afternoon, gone to see a lady about a house.

"She said something else." Miss Loyd brought out another cigarette. He flushed again in recollection, but nevertheless he leaned forward promptly with his lighter. "She said that she was too old; that she should have died long ago; that if she were dead nothing would matter any more."

"She's right about that."

"She meant"–Miss Loyd, dimming behind smoke, sounded oracular–"that nothing would matter for us who were left. The sale of the house, or her death: she puts the two together in her mind. Do you see?"

He shook his head, although in fact he believed he did begin to understand.

"Either one will mean an end to the family. What Mother means to us, what the house means to her . . . it's a kind of chain, I suppose. She finds her identity in the house, seeing it as the last outpost of the rural seat. We who are her children find our identity in her. When she speaks of dying she offers, of course, the last, unanswerable argument of the old. There is no way of fronting up to it. One must go round and slip in by the back door."

"In other words, more strategy?"

"You make it sound so cold-blooded."

"It is."

"Perhaps." She was slipping her arms into her coat sleeves. He got up and found his own coat, and they walked together across the echoing floor. They were silent going down in the elevator, but when they paused in the narrow street foyer, she said, "Well, Mr. Komar, there's the riddle. If you can solve that . . ."

"Then, I may call you?"

"If you like."

There was a touch of shyness in her acquiescence. He was, for a brief but, as it turned out, portentous moment, sharply aware of himself as a man. Yes, his being male was somehow part of the riddle. And Blanche Loyd was still a beautiful woman.

He held open the street door, and she slipped past him. He followed her out, and there in the lee of the building they faced each other. Water ran along the gutters; around them was the commotion of the city. They were poised precipitously on the edge of it, but one last assertion, like a rope flung out, must be made before they could drop safely back into it.

"I will call you," he said with a quick, last confidence.

Impulsively she put out her gloved hand and touched the sleeve of his overcoat. "We seem perpetually to be apologizing to each other, but I say it again: I'm sorry, really sorry, about—oh, about everything. I have wanted to be honest with you. Will you believe me?" She did not wait for his answer. She gave him a hesitant smile and then turned and hurried away toward the corner, an elderly woman stooping behind her umbrella through a November rain.

As he walked on in the opposite direction, now pausing at an intersection, crossing with the light, he found that if this luncheon, following on the events of Monday night, had brutally revealed his incapacity and the ambivalence in his attachments, it had revealed far more importantly the fact that it was himself, Herbert Komar, who was incapable and ambivalent. His spirits quickened. Yes, it was something to learn of oneself, to encounter oneself freshly, urgently, even if one wore the shape of failure. For years the perceptions, the feelings, the musty desires of Herbert Komar had reached him only faintly, submarine shocks from the other side of the globe. Now the ground directly beneath him trembled, and he knew that no matter in which direction he leaped, a fissure might open up and he would plunge through into the ultimate nothing. But he would not look that far ahead. It was enough to take in, just now, the fact of *his* having to leap, of his being actually on the move. To fall even in pain, he found himself thinking (he pushed through a revolving door), was still to know that one had lived. It was a desperate thing to know that one had nowhere to go except forward, yet for the moment, riding up in the elevator, he felt exhilaration even in his discomfort. The Loyds fought, they denounced, they mocked, they were cruel: they were cruel to *him.*

He went along the hallway to his office feeling not gleeful, feeling even a little sad, even tired, and yet . . . He remembered that she had said he might call her, that she had told him not to ask point-blank if the house were for sale.

And yet, he thought.

The qualification was one almost of a grim triumph.

He pushed open the office door.

· 8 ·

BLANCHE Loyd's remark about strategies came into his mind as he slipped out of his coat, stuffed his muffler carefully in the arm, and went into the general office and down its length to his desk. While his exhilaration lasted, he thought, he would determine on a strategy of his own. He would insist upon his corner of the triangle, his right to draw the two lines of the women's separate wills toward himself, to establish a plane on which he would hope to project the structure of their problem, and to see that structure in its dimensions. Miss Loyd had characteristically left the move to him, and he recognized that they should not very rapidly get anywhere if he let almost a week intervene between each meeting.

He was, suddenly, intensely sleepy after the heavy lunch and the cold walk back to work. The telephone rang, and after he had dispatched that he looked down at his desk at the long, crisp interoffice memorandum that one of the stenographers had just laid there. It looked like somebody's last will and testament, and in a quick change of mood he felt bored and exasperated with the amount of work it took to earn the living that one never got round to living. He picked up a pencil and made a series of notations in the margin, and then pulled a stack of papers, bound with a clip, toward him, and slipped down into the darkness of Friday afternoon.

By four-thirty, with still more than an hour to go, for he had been late getting back, he found that not only could he no longer think of the Loyds without a deadly fatigue wiping his mind blank, but he could not even concentrate on the columns and sums of figures that he had always found so absorbing. When Mr. Perry showed him a curious delinquency in the audit of a small manufacturing company whose fiscal year the firm had been closing for over a decade, Mr. Komar felt none of the sense of shock, of concern, of sober elevation, that he would customarily have expected to find in himself. He could not deepen this perfunctory response, and old Perry, in his turn dislodged, turned away with an affectation of indifference quite as much on the surface as was Mr. Komar's show of interest.

But I'm tired, he thought, pushing his pen aside and flipping through his desk calendar for the appointments that were not there, the friends who never called and asked him to dinner. He was momentarily appalled at the number of cold white pages it would take to get through the winter. All I want to do, he said, taking up the pen and drawing a cottage, a tree, a little fence, is to have dinner and then go out to the house and curl up. I'll think about all this when I'm fresher. I don't *have* to buy their house; I don't really need to see them again. There are other houses, other streets, other years than this one. . . .

It did not seem a large request to make of life: this desire simply to curl up. Yet, how often people or events were set on blocking it. His sister Sadie and her husband, for instance, were volubly critical of what he did with his time, and he had long ago resigned himself to bearing their patronage and irritation, for it was true that he was hard put to explain, even to himself, how his evenings, how all his years, passed. To enumerate his small pleasures would have been intolerably embarrassing, and he had no large ones. He did not bowl; he did not go to baseball games or night hockey games; he saw a movie only when a nephew or niece, left on his hands for an evening, dragged him out; he did not play solitaire, either, or build model trains, or collect first-day covers; and though he did not object to a drink, he rarely thought of going into a bar by himself. No, he knew that he practiced none of those reputable diversions that his family seemed to expect from a bachelor. What, he gathered, was at times almost more despicable from their point of view (family pride being what it is) was that he apparently had no disreputable allegiances, either. Indeed, while he had heard men at the office describe their private exploits, he had never found out how they came across these compliant and even urgent creatures whose charms they extravagantly celebrated; and he marveled (he had his pride, too: he marveled secretly) at the celerity with which men in modern novels tumbled into bed with women whom they had met in the very places that he himself frequented: restaurants (he had his breakfast at the house, but he took his other meals out), street corners, buses, the office.

What it came down to, again, was that he liked to curl up;—

but how could he describe to Sadie or his brother-in-law what pleasure he got out of soaking his feet in the tub while he balanced on the edge and read the newspaper? (He only filled the tub a little way, and didn't count it as a bath.) And certainly he could never have told *any*one how he sometimes sat on the toilet for a half hour reading the *Post* or one of Miss Kasco's books. ("Mr. Komar," Mrs. Hlavaty would sometimes say in exasperation, "it's a wonder you don't get piles." The fact was that occasionally he did.) And, after all, how much can you expect to do with a telescoped evening? By the time he'd had dinner and driven out to the house, it was getting toward eight, and it was usually nine when he got out of the bathroom–sometimes later, for he shaved at night to avoid the morning wrangle. A few times a week he took his traveling iron down to Mrs. Hlavaty's board in the kitchen and spent thirty or forty minutes pressing his various pairs of trousers. Often he stretched out for a quick nap, and when he woke it was after eleven and high time to get to bed: he had to be up by six. Some evenings he read a book, or followed a magazine serial, and in the summer he sat out on the front porch and fell asleep there. Occasionally, he had work to do in the evening on his accounts, or some shopping: he explored drugstores and hardware stores minutely, even if he intended to buy no more than a bottle of Arnica or a pair of pliers; or the Chevrolet might need attention, and he would spend a couple of hours down at the garage.

This was how he conducted himself, but nevertheless he did have a feeling, whenever he was challenged, that there must be great gaps in his time that were unaccounted for.

"You know what it's like when you get home," he'd say defensively; and his brother-in-law would answer, "Yeah, *I* know: fix the furnace, Clarence, I been freezin' all day, dry the dishes for me, will ya honey, take out the ashes, Clarence, the rubbish men're coming tomorrow. *I* know."

"Well, I take it easy. I don't have a furnace."

"You're damn lucky," was the response; the censure was unmistakable.

Mr. Komar thought there must be a great many people like himself all over the country, people who were grateful that for a few hours in the day they need not do anything at all. It was true that you never ran across them in books, or on the radio, or in the movies, but he supposed that authors couldn't fashion much drama around men who enjoyed soaking their feet or standing around an icy, smelly garage while a mechanic poked in their car. But when Sadie spoke of people who had certainly better get out of themselves before they turned into downright vegetables, his gall rose. He felt like replying that her bridge club, her dramatics group that never gave plays, the gang she and Clarence chummed around with would, from what he'd seen of them, have profited from a little vegetating. Sometimes, when he had driven up the lakeshore to Lorain to have dinner and spend the evening with them, he had scarcely been able to endure the two or three hours that must pass before he could get his coat and start home. The youngsters fighting over Chinese Checkers or Monopoly; Sadie popping her head around the kitchen door to tell Clarence to let Bert alone with the newspaper, now, come help get these dishes cleared off, and whose turn is it to wash tonight?—is it yours, Rhoda?—Rhoda, you get these done before you go to the show, I can't do everything around here; shirts and blouses and dresses waiting to be ironed in the dining room; the telephone ringing and Clarence telling Eddie or Lois June for God's sake get off that phone, don't you think somebody else might want to use it?—he had wondered how these busy people endured their incessant commotion. He had thought longingly of his quiet room, everything in place, his book or magazine spread open on his bed, his clothes laid out for morning, and the beautiful, solemn, empty evening lying before him, to use as he chose, to be ended when he wished it to end.

And now, sitting at his desk with the sound around him of

everyone getting ready to go home—purses snapping shut, the washroom doors swinging perpetually back and forth, car keys and bus tokens jingling, women pulling on galoshes, and expectation running like a night wind among the abandoned desks (the interior people going back to their boxes, he thought sadly)—and now he only wanted the silence of his own rented box, the reassurance of the lamp on his nightstand shedding its light across his cheerful, nubbly bedspread, and of the radiator clanking and sending off its damp, metal-smelling warmth and its occasional spray of hot, rusty water.

He did not want to out-strategize Blanche Loyd.

He worked until well after six, and then he closed his books and went out to dinner. The rush hour was over, the city as dark and empty as if, behind its lightless panes, a remnant population waited in silence for an occupation to come, just as silently, in. This was a city in which no one lived, and it struck him, as he walked along the sidewalks to the restaurant, as somehow both sad and terrible, this daily human evacuation. An occasional bus hurried along the middle of the street, a few last refugees jiggling inside it, their faces peering hostilely out the windows. In the deserted buildings wood and plaster models in pretty clothes stared blankly at him from lighted showcases. Only the restaurants still maintained a semblance of life: people eating downtown before they went to the movies, or, like himself, tenants of solitary rooms picking up dinner before they went home. What a pity! he thought, and, indeed, he did regret the absence of apartments and houses in the downtown section. Once, coming out of his building after having worked until nearly midnight, he had been struck by the non-humanity and the pitiable, human helplessness of stone and metal and wood devoid of the men who had built them. Their value was that they had no certain mortality, but this also was their damnation. A cat had sat on the sidewalk, licking its paws. Where did it live? he had wondered. Who cared for it, who loved it, after the fall of night? With whom, with what, did it consort? He had had a fantastic vision of the cat reveling in a dark cellar with the enormous rats that crept up from the lakefront and infested the older buildings. Thousands of bright, malicious eyes, the scutter of light feet on cement, a babel of small voices; and hairy shadows stealing up to the street, dancing along the streetcar tracks, overwhelming a motorman on his solitary night run. Cats and rats careering through the midnight city, running up the arm of a dummy in a department store window, rolling in silks, sitting on counters in empty restaurants, and no one to see them, no one to stop them. He had gone along the pavement that night, wishing, wishing that he might pass a house where curtains blew softly in an urbane wind, and a burst of music from a radio turned too loud fell down on the head of the passerby. But this was a daylight city, he thought again, and the buildings, he almost believed, sensed each evening their imminent desertion and shrank away from the brutal pavements, away from the caterwauling rats and cats and the midnight streetcars grinding empty through the empty maze.

During his dinner he began to feel again some of the brief rising of his spirits of the afternoon, and he surrendered himself to the problem of the Loyds. It was when, once more, he expressed to himself the necessity of *out*-strategizing Blanche Loyd that he began to get hold of a plan. For it occurred to him, as he ate his dish of asparagus in drawn butter and pursued the last crumbs from the breaded pork chop, that his own hesitancy about taking a step was based at least in part on his impression that he and Miss Loyd had, for the time, said all to each other that there was to say. Miss Loyd had shut the front door; she had, it was true, encouragingly tossed him the key, but the door was stuck. He remembered her metaphor of going around to the back, and as he began on the raisin pie he suddenly understood that he must bypass her for the present; he must get hold of someone else in the household. But whom? He was reluctant to involve himself with the old woman; she was as subtle a strategist as her daughter, he suspected, and even more efficient at keeping the door shut. She might—he credited her with this much humor—she might toss him a key, but it would probably release only the padlock on the coal hole. There remained only one other possibility, the housekeeper, Mrs. Mentone. He thought that from her he might gather some idea of the issues that were involved. She had, he understood, been with the Loyds for some time; and that night at the house he had observed on her part a degree of familiarity with the family that, if it was unexpected, might nevertheless prove valuable.

And then, having determined on the object of his strategy, his energy flagged before the necessity of having to put the plan into action. He left the restaurant telling himself that he would let it jell of its own volition; he would temporarily dissociate himself from it; in fact, his quick surrender to a plan had given new strength to his inertia. Peace and quiet: he asked of life no more, and to struggle . . . was any object ever worth a great struggle? Did not, he wondered, getting into his car, the really desirable things of life come easily or not at all? He had noticed even in his small circle that the people whom one liked, the people who were relaxed and genial and contented, had got that way through no extraordinary effort. Good luck and fortune had, one generally discovered, fallen to their lot: uncles died leaving handsome bequests, shares went up in value, insurance policies came due. The strugglers, the malcontents: they were the ones—contrary to the Loyds' view—whose presence put an intolerable burden not only on themselves but on others, no matter how successful, by a material scale, they could be weighed in. He found young people a great strain with their exasperations, their intolerances, their determination: they would arrive where they set out for, with luck, but where would they be? What, for that matter, had their convictions ever done for Blanche Loyd and her mother?

He remembered having read years ago that whatever crosses a man crosses him for good or ill, and a man had better be crossed only with the best if he is to develop the best he has in him. He thought that was true: hardship, rebellion, ambition never made a finer person of anyone. And when a man of his own age was seized with the desire to struggle, to assert himself, could there be any positive outcome? Would he not simply wear himself down, or, as he had said to Blanche Loyd, use up in his effort the last of the precious fluid in the bottle?

It was a half hour's drive from the downtown section to the south side. Mr. Komar bumped through the lighted Public Square, and drove on west toward the bridge over the broad and shallow industrial valley which separated the city proper from the west and southern suburbs. A fine, chalky haze was drifting off the lake, and the sounds of automobile horns, of streetcar wheels, of a plane crossing the sky, had the hollow and extended mournfulness that always presages rain; or, in this case, more rain. He passed a drugstore, a State employment agency; as he paused for a light he saw a sign spread across the lower windows of an office building: "Loft for rent. Three thousand cubic feet. Immediate occupancy."

The light changed, but it was the horn on the car behind him that made Mr. Komar let in the clutch and roll forward. The sign had projected him back into his difficulty. Dwellers in a house of stone: there was something blasphemous in this conception of Blanche Loyd's. On another level it was the kind of blasphemy that made idiots and geniuses proclaim themselves gods. Rooms for living and dying in, and the clamorous mob at the door. He thought himself too old, too wise for struggle, but there was a panic in his heart when he thought that she saw him, too, as only distinguished from these others because he wanted—ah! how absurd the whole thing was!—her house, *her* cubic feet.

Yet, as the Chevrolet scuttled across the bridge and turned left into the busy street that skirted the western rim of the valley for several miles, he was struck by how much the city did resemble a vast and disorganized house. He had never seen Paris or Venice, and did not think he ever would; he had not even been to New York,—but he had the impression that in these other, greater stone houses men had occasionally built with an eye toward beauty and pleasure. The streets of his own city proclaimed nothing more valuable than utility: smoke stacks, streetcar rails, overhead wires, traffic islands, bus stops, subway exits. There was no spirit, no wit here, and the people, rolled flat and featureless by the monster they had created, were also devoid of wit and gaiety, impossible to distinguish among. And he, too? he wondered again, with his neat room, his pleasant, absorbing routine? And he, too?

What was it that made the Loyds unique? For after all he had to recognize that their conviction had in some way acted upon them, so that among the interior people whom he knew they alone blazed out. But that was the wrong way to put it, for one might pass Blanche Loyd on the sidewalk and never notice her. No, it was not obtrusiveness in a crowd that was her distinction. It was, rather, an assurance about her and her mother that, dwelt upon, impressed one more and more deeply—an understanding one arrived at that the sooty interior of this house of rock and steel, this efficient metropolis, would never weigh on them. Subsist in it they must, but in return they would give it nothing except the ignorance that it deserved.

Ah! he could not get it all in. He thought of Mary Bush: she was the embodiment, with her blue eyes, her joyous hardihood. He saw her there—in front of the old market building, or there, on a traffic island—and she was buoyant; she lifted her arms and the mist curled around her, a gentlest veil. How she laughed! And as he peered through his wet-beaded windshield and stopped now for a light, now for a slowing streetcar, he had the impression that if he looked quickly to the left he would see a figure running, dancing through the mist in the dark shadow of the blacker buildings, and that if he could retain his vision long enough the brick and stone would prove illusory, they would show that they too had no defense except men's belief in them. The mist would melt into day, and where the buildings had stood, rank on rank, there would be hills that were green with young trees in the sunlight, and grassy plains falling like waves into the horizon, and far away would be the breaking sound of surf.

But, magically, the radiant figure was gone from this landscape. He saw only the rising sun, the green combers, the buoyant, crowned hills, and he felt a stirring peace; there was no need even to revolt against revolt; and it was not simplicity that he embraced, it was not any longer a surrender that he made in his ambivalence.

But an oncoming streetcar clanged its metal bell at him, and he realized that he was driving straight toward it. And what in heaven's name was he thinking about? (He swerved aside and pressed the accelerator toward the floor. The Chevrolet flew past a lingering bus, past rows of parked automobiles, flew from the vision, from its meaning.) He was suddenly, coldly, shocked by his fancy; it seemed to him not only irrelevant but, in its implications, senile. (Here someone shouted, and he realized the last disaster had come upon him: he had driven through a red light.)

As a boy he had played at pirate; he had assumed the role of any glorious ruffian whom he encountered in a book, and it had not taken much effort to transform the parlor table into a round, brown island floating in a green sea of light, and the vapor lamp in the center had become the volcano in whose side treasure lay dangerously buried. But all that was forty, fifty years behind him; he had passed eagerly into the swamp of adolescence, leaving his bright, firm dreams where they properly belonged; and as he had picked his way toward the innocence of youth and emerged finally into the greater innocence of adulthood, he had not often felt the need of some vision, some affirmation that no one could touch—least of all that most dangerous huntsman, himself. He was frightened to think that he was coming full circle. He remembered his mother during her last days in the Home, calling him by an old lover's name, slipping with a sad finality into that tongue that she had long disclaimed any knowledge of, dressing herself, when she was allowed, like a girl, and waiting for one of her children with a smile of bright expectation on her wrinkled, furry mouth. It had been terrible, terrible; until this last week he had never felt so much alone as when she grasped his hand and called him eagerly by that other name, and he had resented he thought rightly her last happiness (she had slipped away from them like a girl going out to marriage, and in her final sleep the faint, delighted chuckles had given way only to the painful rattling of death).

Was he, too, approaching that sad last state of illusion? He refused the responsibility of his vision, even as he denied its import. It was Blanche Loyd's work, as it had been she who drove him to the bathroom looking glass, and away from it again, defeated. And this he would struggle against, this kind of surrender. He would save himself; the lady with the blue eyes was dead, dead.

And here, now, it was raining, one of those silent rains that seem far away, far away, shutting one heavily in. He crossed another bridge over a spur of the valley and entered the desolation of suburban streets.

He passed a row of minor industries—pottery, screws and bolts, mirrors made or resilvered, fencing—the little buildings sodden under the November rain. On his left were the homes that are the inevitable accompaniment of this kind of enterprise: solitary frame houses that stood close to the sidewalk and appeared to mourn for their lost front porches and their vanished barns, and hard rows of newer houses, shingle, clapboard, or tapestry brick scored with picture windows that afforded the occupants a full view of the screw and bolt plant opposite.

He passed along this utilitarian length and turned into the broad thoroughfare, bleakly illuminated by droplights on poles, that was his own street. Under the falling rain the houses looked as if they had been disinterred from muddy graves. The street had been built up over a period of forty years, and in their spacing and size the houses evidenced a democratic scorn for zoning and building restrictions. Large, three-storied dwellings with corner towers and mansard roofs stretched to the edges of their tiny lots; behind some of them, crowding up almost to their back steps, were the smaller ones that had been put on the property first. Halfway along the street was a wooden terrace that flanked the grounds of a sprawling, one-story cottage set behind a dwindled orchard; on the farther side of the cottage was a shingled duplex, and beyond that, at still a different remove from the pavement, a brick bungalow that had gone up the year before. So the pattern, with infinite architectural variations, repeated itself all along the street, on both sides.

The older houses—victims today of that spacious era which had given them rise—had generally been converted into doubles or housekeeping apartments. A few of the shabbier ones retained single families; and a fair number of others were, like Mrs. Hlavaty's, stuffed full of elderly bachelors, schoolteachers whose native habitat was invariably Indiana or the coal regions of southern Ohio, and transient, boisterous couples who had no children.

In summer, when the old trees along the curb were full, the disparity in the houses' grouping and the vulgarity in their architecture were obscured; and the street lamps, blooming softly out of dusty foliage, gave to the tarred and pebbled surface of the roadway a faintly rural quality. Then, the residents, sitting on their front porches behind massed syringa bushes or honeysuckle and trumpet vines on wire trellises, might almost have believed—as, indeed, they remarked to each other—that it was just like the country. In fact, the hush and the uneven darkness were of a sort which no countryside can produce: they are the property only of streets buried deep in a city.

The quality of city-ness was everywhere on this stripped winter night: in the glistening, empty pavement; in the glitter of tree trunks under the street lamps; in the endless, straight marching poles; in the innumerable glowing windows. The quality, perhaps, was one of emptiness and expectation, and of a fulfillment that would never come.

Although Mrs. Hlavaty's bulky and shapeless house stood back a considerable distance from the sidewalk, its neighbors on either side jostled it so closely that it appeared almost to have been funneled onto its foundation. The first floor was clapboarded, but the overlapping second and third were faced by octagonal brown shingles that gave to the whole building an effect of precarious overbalance.

On the south side of the house, a dining room bay launched itself over a narrow sandstone walk. From her rocking chair here, it was Mrs. Hlavaty's custom to survey the activities five feet away in her neighbor's dining room. Mr. Komar wondered occasionally whether the inspection was reciprocal. If it was, he knew that the results for the other people were disappointing: there were never any rolls of dust under Mrs. Hlavaty's buffet, such as she soberly reported having seen across the way, nor was there any irregularity in the hour of meals, or a failure to clear off the table directly dinner was over.

On the north side, a driveway squeezed between the foundation of Mrs. Hlavaty's house and that of an immense, turreted and sun-porched bungalow. It led to a stable that stood at the rear property line. Some former owner had converted the stable into a double garage, and it was here that Mr. Komar left his car.

As he turned into the drive, the front porch light came on. One of Mrs. Hlavaty's many economies was saving on electricity (a late-returning lodger had either to grope his way upstairs through blackness or flick the hall switch and resign himself to a barrage of humorous remarks from his landlady the following morning); the only times when the porch was lit were when the paper boy came to collect and when Mrs. Hlavaty was entertaining with an evening of Hearts. As he put the car in the garage Mr. Komar tried to remember whether she had mentioned anything to him; he was certain she had not. Her parties were often last-minute affairs, however, and probably at this moment she was hovering around the back door, waiting to pounce on him as soon as he got into the kitchen.

"My good land, Mr. Komar," he imagined her saying (he shut off the motor and pushed the gear into second), "I was about ready to give you up! I suppose I should have called you at the office, but I didn't think you'd be as late as this."

"Did you want me for something, Mrs. Hlavaty?" he heard himself ask. (He got out and closed the garage doors.)

"Why, I'm having a few friends in tonight. I hope you're free to join us."

He would pretend he had just understood her. "Why, that'll be very pleasant. It's nice of you to think of me. I was held up at the office, but if you'll just let me run upstairs a minute, I'll be ready. Can I give you a hand with the card table?"

And, yes, he thought, it would be pleasant to spend an evening at the card table. This, too, was part of his routine; this, too, would give him a measure of reassurance that his mind, circling restlessly through its self-constructed maze, could not give him.

He hurried through the rain to the back steps, an anticipatory smile already on his face. Through the glass he could see Mrs. Hlavaty: there she was, energetically wiping off the stove.

He burst inside as if a gale were at his back.

"What a night!" he exclaimed cheerfully. He swept off his glasses and began to polish them with the fingers of his glove. "We've really had about every kind of weather this week, haven't we?"

"Goodness, Mr. Komar! You gave me a start! I didn't hear your car come in."

He could barely suppress his amusement. This was her customary tactic. "I got my plugs cleaned Wednesday," he replied. He sat down and pulled off his rubbers. "I guess she's quieter now."

"I knew you were up to something," Mrs. Hlavaty remarked disconcertingly, "out three nights in five. I said to Mr. Vogel just before you drove in, 'You see if I'm not right,' I said; 'Mr. Komar's got some bee in his bonnet.' "

"Why, Myron should have known where I was," Mr. Komar said, beginning to understand that he and his landlady were embarked on quite different strategies. "I told him Tuesday that I was going to get my gearshift fixed and see what else needed doing."

"Well, I said it was certainly none of my business. 'Mr. Komar's life is his own,' I said." Mrs. Hlavaty wrenched the drippings pan out of the broiler and carried it to the sink.

Mr. Komar watched her broad back, divided into squares and rectangles by the straps of her apron, with a sensation of helpless bafflement. Had he not been certain that she had no reason to find fault with him, he would have judged that she was angry. Indeed, he began to feel much as he had in the presence of Lily Loyd: as if he had committed some unpardonable trespass which would never be explained, but which he would pay for dearly.

"I worked late at the office," he said, trying to keep his voice level and undisturbed, and still make it audible above the roar of tap water and the clattering of the pan against the porcelain sink.

There was no reply; he thought he probably imagined the stiffening in Mrs. Hlavaty's heavy, muscular arms. Certainly, it was absurd to think that her brilliantly red hair bristled at him, as if each strand had a nerve at its end, and each nerve was assaulted by this barefaced lie.

He looked at the kitchen table. There was the inevitable chopping bowl full of onions and celery and green peppers; beside it were the usual tins of not-quite-finest-grade tuna fish, and the bottle of mayonnaise.

"Looks like you're having a get-together," he said loudly.

The faucet was turned off. Mrs. Hlavaty hauled the pan out of the sink and dried it swiftly with a dishrag. She avoided looking at him, and undeniably there was a grim set to her jaw. "Just the usual," she replied. Her footsteps shook the floor as she crossed it and restored the pan to the broiler. "I'd have said something to you, but you're such a gadabout these days I didn't know if it'd be convenient for you." She picked up the coffee pot and carried it back with her.

He got up with his rubbers and walked over to the stove. Mrs. Hlavaty never cared to have the boarders put their overshoes in the front vestibule when she was expecting guests. He was accustomed to putting them under the stove at such times, and then to moving them again after the company had gone. He bent over, grateful for this cover for his disappointment, and arranged the rubbers as carefully as if they had been intended for display.

"It's just as well you didn't count on me. I've got some work to do this evening. November's always a heavy month for us." He straightened up and groped for an exit line that would carry him across the expanse of gleaming linoleum and through the dining room door. "Well, it's certainly a crazy night."

"I never let the weather get me down," Mrs. Hlavaty said. (She was now engaged in scrubbing the sides of the coffee pot with cleanser—a treatment he was certain it had not received since the day it was brought home from the dimestore.) "Besides, November's always a funny month, isn't it? Of course, you're out a lot more than I am."

"Yes," he agreed; "that makes a difference." He paused in the dining room doorway and arranged a casual smile, although she was not looking. "Now, don't let them give you any wooden nickels."

Mrs. Hlavaty visibly stiffened. "There's no need for that caution here, Mr. Komar. If my guests want to play for money, they can go somewhere else. Not in *my* house, they won't!"

"It's just a saying," he explained (and he remembered the singularly unfortunate toasts he had proposed at luncheon; plainly, this was not his day). "You know, like bottoms up."

"Not in *my* house," said Mrs. Hlavaty. "No gambling and no drinking, either. I'm just a little surprised you'd think that, Mr. Komar."

Something—perhaps this double humiliation of the afternoon and evening—prompted him to make matters as bad as possible. "I guess you never know."

"Indeed you do *not!*" She laughed grimly.

He turned away, but he had got no further than the dining room table when Mrs. Hlavaty exclaimed, "Why, whoever left *these* here?"

He saw that she was looking at his rubbers. He came back a few steps. "I believe they're mine," he replied after a moment, with the same fine indirection. "I thought you'd rather not have me put them out in the vestibule."

"Isn't that just like a man?" Mrs. Hlavaty implored. "With a whole empty back porch, he brings them in on my clean floor. In this weather it's all I can do to keep this house halfway decent; and I can't do it by myself, now, can I?"

He picked up the rubbers and deposited them outside the back door. He began to understand just how notable a victory it was for Miss Kasco to do her laundry in the bathroom. Still, there was no use arguing; something had got the old girl's wind up: tomorrow it would have blown itself out, and for breakfast he'd have an extra egg.

Mrs. Hlavaty was filling the coffee pot when he came in again. He abandoned dignity and hurried past her into the dining room; but here he paused again. She should not confound him as easily as this.

"Have a good time," he said.

"What?" she asked. She turned away from the sink briefly; it was plain that she was astonished to find him still lingering. "Oh! Why, we always do, don't we? Will you close that door after you, Mr. Komar? At this rate, I'm never going to get ready in time."

He passed through the deserted front hall and climbed wearily up the stairs. On the landing he met Mildred Kasco. She was wearing a nubbly green suit with a white linen collar whose tapering ends made her long face look even longer. The suit, he knew, was reserved for special occasions: P.T.A. parties and meetings of the North Eastern Ohio Teachers' Association. The odor of gardenia was strong upon her. She had evidently doused the tiny corsage of red strawflowers that clung to one of the points of her collar.

"Joining us tonight, Mr. Komar?" she asked brightly.

"Good evening. No, I don't believe so; not tonight." He looked at the suit, and contrasted it with the stark black wool dress that Blanche Loyd had worn at luncheon—with the old-fashioned sunburst at the throat. "You're looking all trimmed up," he said.

He knew what was coming by the great wave of gardenia that broke across him. Miss Kasco had a very delicate sensibility, and was eager to find offence.

"Just how do you mean that, Mr. Komar?"

Just the way it sounds! he thought defiantly. You look like a roll of carpeting.

"I mean, isn't that your new suit?"

"This?" Mollified, she glanced down at herself. "It isn't doing me any good hanging in the closet, is it?"

She seemed determined not to let him pass. She was a narrow stick of a woman, but tall—taller by a good three inches than he was. She transfixed him with a slate-gray eye, and in a voice of sly triumph said, "I guess you've got a lot to keep you busy these days. Out all hours: I was saying to Mrs. Hlavaty that I wouldn't be surprised if we lost Mr. Komar one of these days."

"Oh?" he asked. "Why would you think that?"

"I can tell," she replied enigmatically. "Well, everybody thinks of himself first, doesn't he?"

"I guess so. In my case, there isn't anybody else."

"That's right. As Mrs. Hlavaty said, you've got your own life to live."

"She told you that, too?"

"Just how do you mean that?"

"I mean that she told Myron Vogel the same thing."

"Yes, I believe I did hear her mention it to him. *I* said that I certainly thought you were lucky. Most of us have to think twice before we do something."

"Yes," he agreed stubbornly, "I suppose I am lucky."

The irregular patches of rouge on her thin cheeks glowed under her determination to dig deep, and as he started to pass her and go on up the steps she put out one of her astonishingly long arms and caught his sleeve. "It's none of my business, Mr. Komar, but I do think you ought to have a little bit of consideration for Mrs. Hlavaty. She hasn't had an easy time of it, you know."

He swung round abruptly, brushing her hand off his sleeve. "The one thing I *do* know, Miss Kasco, is that I haven't any idea what you're talking about. I worked late at the office tonight, if that interests you. Furthermore, I am Mrs. Hlavaty's boarder, not"—he brought out clumsily—"her servant."

"*Ser*vants!" she said. "I guess you *are* moving out of our class! I guess Mrs. Hlavaty was right to feel you wouldn't care to join us this evening. And pardon *me! Par*don me! *I*'m only a boarder here. It doesn't matter that we've always felt like a family in this house. Naturally, when your interests take you elsewhere, you haven't time for the people you leave behind." And she moved haughtily past him, as if it had been he who blocked the landing.

It was incredible, he thought, watching Miss Kasco jerk down the stairs, how women could distort what one said: and not unconsciously, but with a deliberate audacity that left one helpless to refute them. He thought of Mrs. Hlavaty seizing on his remark about wooden nickels and turning it into a premeditated insult; and now this swift misinterpretation of "servant." He had no doubt that the story would be developed during the course of the evening. He saw himself surrounded by women: by his landlady, by her inquisitive boarder, by the Loyds. Mary Bush! he thought, going up three steps to the hall, how you would laugh at all this. And as he looked at the long, narrow hallway with its cream-colored wallpaper and sparse hanging of narrow pictures and monstrous Currier and Ives calendars, his vision of sunlit fields flooded the cold space, and he did not deny it. He stepped forward. Then, from the foot of the stairs, Mildred Kasco spoke to him.

"Did Mrs. Hlavaty give you your call?" she asked, not succeeding entirely in her attempt to sound brisk, cold, incurious.

"Call?" He let himself be drawn back into the sunless interior. He leaned over the railing and made a great effort to sound as if nothing unpleasant had occurred between them. "No, she didn't. Was it my sister?"

"I wouldn't know. She probably left a note on your bed."

"You're slipping, Miss Kasco," he said, and as he withdrew he saw outrage written plain across her features. He almost chuckled as he went along the corridor to his room.

On his bedspread there was indeed a note in Mrs. Hlavaty's round, unpracticed script: "Mrs. Mentoan called 6.30. Mrs. Lloyd would like to see you Mon. nite about that matter—said to call her back tonite if pos."

Mrs. Loyd! What could she want to see him for? And Mrs. Mentone as bearer of the message: God knew how much waggling her tongue had done that Mrs. Hlavaty had left out of the note. He understood now why he had been excluded from the evening of Hearts, why the encounter with Mildred Kasco. He knew from experience that there was no more suspicious person than a landlady: the more genteel she is, the more hospitable and interested, the more is she determined never to let go of you. When you threaten to slip away, she exhumes past dinners and hot water bottles and confidences and, as it were, returns them tied in a black ribbon; and if her eyes, as she lays down her generous bundle, are sharp with resentfulness and curiosity, they are veiled, and her voice and manner are heavy with forgiveness. It is the strong-willed boarder who will throw all this back in a lady's face and depart without a longer consideration. He may tell himself that over the years he has paid into her till many thousands of dollars, that he has done without frequent baths because the flowing away of all that hot water nearly breaks her heart, that he has obediently left his rubbers to congeal in the vestibule and denied himself guests because of the bathroom situation; but still he cannot free himself from the hundreds of cans of tuna fish he has consumed, the boilers-full of coffee; he remembers the liver pills she has made him take, the hot lemonade she has personally brought to his feverish bed, the times she called the office to say he was too sick to come in.

He had detected these predatory attitudes in Mrs. Hlavaty when he first rented a room from her, but he had believed that as the years went by her suspicions had died away. He had come to think of her as a friend, as someone he would wish to go on seeing, even if he settled in a home of his own ("I'm having a few people in for pinochle and I wondered . . ."). He was hurt and dismayed to see that their relationship was not one whit altered by this ten years' close residence. It appeared instead that the passing of so much time had only made him more suspect in her estimation.

He felt a little ill, standing and looking at the portentous note. He wondered suddenly about all human relationships. Was one ever valued for oneself? He knew that his relations with Mrs. Hlavaty would never be the same, whether he stayed on with her for another ten years or she finally brought herself to bless his venture. He looked around the small room: the walls hardened into unfamiliar outlines, the furniture became impersonal, indifferent to him now that the fact of his sometime leaving it was established; the rugs on the floor, the picture of Cupid on the wall, the radiator with its metal cover: a rented room, a house of business.

He thought wryly of the deceptions he had practiced in the course of this decade. They had been designed to remove this very stigma of business, of impersonality: leaving his five dollars on the pillow, so that Mrs. Hlavaty could take it without there having to be any remarking between them on the exchange, giving her a box of candy at Easter, flowers at Christmas. He alone had been deceived.

He rose and took off his coat and threw it across the bed. He did not feel angry. He did not blame Mrs. Hlavaty because in a last analysis he was only a source of income. He knew that he made too much of things (or too little? his mind interpolated ironically). And he thought, as he crossed to the bureau, that the character of the landlady could be set down on almost anyone else, and that with a few minor alterations it would fit. So, with small attentions, his own relatives bound him to their side; but when he died they would shake their heads (a little reprovingly) and consign him to the photograph album or the stand-up frame on the tier-table, and speculate on how much the old boy had put by all these years.

Yet, he asked himself, with an effort at honesty, what have I ever given, generously, freely?—and he could think of nothing. He had given to his mother in his role as a son, to his sister as a brother, to Mrs. Hlavaty precisely because he, too, knew himself to be a boarder. And if always there had been in his intention a something more, had he ever succeeded in making it manifest? He looked at himself with a real curiosity as he stood before the bureau looking glass, and this time his eyes did not flicker aside, and no quick, frantic humor twisted his lips. He saw the pale blue eyes and the short, fine lashes, the irregular, colorless brows, the long nose, the mouth: broad, narrow-lipped; the oval, retreating jaw. Not a memorable face. Not a memorable man. Herbert Komar. There is Herbert Komar. But I . . . he thought, I too am the something else, the something more. That is not all of me. But he knew that here in the glass was reflected all that anyone else ever saw. *He keeps himself to himself.* Who had said that? He could not remember. A girl: it was a girl's voice . . . long ago. Yes, it would have been a great while ago;

and he heard the accusation she made. He thought it funny that Herbert Komar should have so little self to keep to. If the girl had known. If she had only known. . . .

He sat down in the cretonne chair beside his nightstand and took off his shoes and stockings. The practice, so homely and familiar and reassuring, almost shook him back into his somnolence. But as his bare feet touched the cold floor he was struck afresh by this sense of being alien and alone. He knew he had nowhere to go except forward.

He got into his slippers and went out into the hall. The upstairs phone stood at the far end, at the top of the stairs. He got his wallet out of his pocket and removed the slip of paper that had the Loyds' number on it. As he sat down before the stand, he heard a charge of laughter explode in the living room; Myron Vogel's deep voice boomed up the well, "Two no trump!"

Why, he thought, they aren't even playing Hearts! And resolutely, with a greater calmness than he felt, he began to dial the Loyds' number. What would he do, he wondered—(he'd never heard one of Mrs. Hlavaty's parties sound so successful)—if Blanche Loyd answered? But he felt that he scarcely cared; he would ask for Mrs. Mentone. Perhaps Miss Loyd would not recognize his voice: she would be perfectly capable, at least, of pretending she did not.

But it was Mrs. Mentone who picked up the receiver.

"This is Herbert Komar. I believe you tried to get in touch with me?"

"Oh, yes, Mr. Komar. Mrs. Loyd asked me to call you about the—the arrangements. I suppose you know what she's talking about?"

"I believe so."

"That's good. They don't tell me anything around here, but I guess I can put a few things together!"

"She'd like to see me Monday?"

"If that's convenient for you. Any time you're free."

"Has Miss Loyd been speaking to her, do you happen to know?"

"They're speaking right now. Can't tell how long it'll last." Mrs. Mentone giggled.

"No, I meant about the—arrangements."

"I couldn't tell you. They don't tell me a thing."

"I thought you might have noticed. Tonight, for instance? . . ."

"Tonight? No, I'm sure about that. Blanche hasn't got home yet. She's having her hair done. Big party coming up. No, this is just between you and Mrs. Loyd—and me."

"I see. Well, thank you. I'll try to get there by seven-thirty or eight."

"Seven-thirty? That will be . . ." There was a slight hesitation, and he remembered that the telephone was in the living room.

"Mrs. Loyd wonders if you'd mind making it a little after eight—just to be on the safe side?"

"Yes. Certainly."

"Then that's all right. Thank you for calling, Mr. Komar."

He went slowly back to his room. "Just to be on the safe side." What strategy lay behind that remark? He felt himself slipping down, the loose shale skidding away from his clutching fingers, and he looked below him and saw nothing except darkness and murderous space. With a last burst of rebellion he slammed his bedroom door on the world, but he was not quick enough to escape the shriek of triumph from the living room, or Mrs. Hlavaty's hearty "Time out! Who'll give me a hand with the lunch?"

PART FOUR

Interval

· 9 ·

THE SKY, on that Monday in November, 1938, was a remote, variable blue: a milk-glass bowl across the slope of which moved not the sun, it seemed, but its cream-colored, insubstantial reflection. The shadows of the tall stone buildings shifted across the bands of sidewalk and street, and in the lake a north wind sent the gray-green waves ruffling against the breakwater. Even within the bay the waters welled and sank uneasily, cracking and drowning the skin of ice along the shore.

The north wind flew low over the docks, over the shipyards, over the railroad tracks; it funneled into the streets of the city, and people at intersections bent double against it, and spread their legs to keep themselves erect. They fled into doorways, but the wind followed inexorably, and, as they dug at soot in their eyes, it snatched at their hats, at the flap in their coats, at their packages. Winddrift newspapers eddied along the pavement, darted wildly at small children and old ladies, raced to extinction under the wheels of trucks and buses.

Toward midafternoon this ground wind died abruptly, and with it, for a time, the larger city sounds: the grind and clangor of streetcars, the plunging roar of traffic. What was audible was the clatter of a woman's heels, the grunt of a revolving door, the rattling of a sign in its metal socket: but these served merely to measure the depth of the immediate silence. Above the buildings, bulky clouds circled and grazed each other in a ritual of mating. Then, somewhere, a motorman struck his bell: noise flooded back into the void, and presently a fine, heavy sleet flung itself against the lighted windows of offices, hotels, theaters, rebounded, and plunged thirty stories to the shining brick and asphalt and concrete. The owners of newspaper stands snatched them up from in front of cigar stores, and hauled them into narrow, dim interiors where the glaring headlines of that glaring age faced through the dusk the calm and frozen features of Prince Albert and the lady of La Palina cigars. REICH OFFERS CURB ON WAR PLANES, GAS said the headlines, but Prince Albert was dead and did not care, and the lady, lucky for her, was a fiction whom fact could never confound. The proprietors cursed the weather: bad for business, death on business, hope to God it clears by five.

In her office Blanche Loyd sighed as the door fell shut behind Mr. Morris, who sold slicing machines from his cubicle on the second floor. Because he had no secretary, hardly making enough, poor man, to live on himself, and because he had been almost the first tenant she met when she moved into the building (their offices, his more flourishing then, hers more modest, had faced each other across the hall)—because of these things she wrote his business letters for him, extolling hand slicers, motorized slicers, plain and colored, chromium trim extra. The letters, turbulent in their grammar, grew more ill-tempered in their tone every year; and every year she found him more difficult to deal with and more pitiably dependent on her recognition of his position as a man of business. He liked to catch her out on small errors. He would wait in her office in an agony of impatience while she typed his letters, and then seize them fresh from the roller and hurry, as best he could at seventy-five, down to his own office, and there, presumably, go over them word by word, a sheet of paper laid along each line to mask the lines that followed. Then, up he would come again, and point to where she had struck a "g" instead of an "h." In his meticulous, unreadable Spencerian script he would make the correction at her desk. He did not know, she hoped he would never learn, that two-page, single-spaced letters, of a kind which no one ever waded through any longer, cost more than fifty cents.

She switched on her desk lamp and looked at the ragged bundle of poems that Mr. Day, who had rented an office from her back when, for a few years during the war, she had had a suite, had left for her to transform into a neat manuscript, suitable for the eyes of an editor, and three carbons, please.

Dark, dark the deep,
And down–
Falling,
Falling . . .

she read. What deep? What fall? She turned off the light, too tired to type the poems now, and shut her eyes. The rush of the city rose seven floors and hovered, a clamorous spectre, against her window, and the gray sleet was falling, falling.–Dark, dark the deep, and down, falling.

At four-fifteen, in the house in Grant Street, Mrs. Mentone entered the living room. The storm rustled against the broad panes, and the gas fire protested like the old woman in her dreams.

"Time for *Stella Dallas,* Mother!" she said. "My goodness, it's like the black hole in here! Don't you want some light?" But the old woman did not reply. She was asleep. "Oh, well," said Mrs. Mentone. She pushed in the blanket around Lily's legs, and quietly retreated. Ten minutes later she came speeding down the back stairs. "Lou," she said to her husband, who was sitting at the kitchen table over a cup of coffee, "I wish you'd take a look in the attic. I was in the bathroom, and there was a *bump*. . . ."

At Mr. Komar's office a party was getting under way. One of the girls was leaving to be married, and they had all gone together and bought her a really exquisite evening bag and a little, square, gold compact.

"Oh, I'm simply *thrilled!*" she cried. "I certainly didn't expect

. . . *look* at it coming down! I just hate to take these things out . . . why, Mr. Briskin, I guess you *can!* I'm not a married woman yet!"—and prettily she put her narrow face up for her boss's kiss. The office gang smirked, and it was a good thing it was after four: plainly, nobody would do another lick of work before closing time.

At Mrs. Hlavaty's, Miss Kasco shook off her galoshes in the vestibule and burst open the glass door into the front hall.

"Yoo-hoo!" she called. "Anybody h—? Oh, there you are. Any news? I was dying to ask you at breakfast, but with *him* there I knew you couldn't say anything. I thought I'd die laughing. Did you catch my look? Wait'll I get my coat off. Isn't this weather the *limit?* I'm *soaked!*"

So, all over the city, ladies typed, turned on *Stella Dallas,* hung wet coats in front of ovens; girls powdered their nose, and came out of the washroom saying, "Has it let up yet?"; file clerks glanced furtively at their tiny watches; restaurant hostesses, with practiced smiles already on their mouths, stood beside innumerable brass poles and velvet cords, waiting like showgirls for the five o'clock performance; and a thousand white city faces pressed impatiently against the gray city windows, spectators to the dying fall of sleet through the dying light. Between five-ten and five-eleven, almost at the moment when Steve Kovac, an unemployed trucker, shot dead his wife Ruth and the man he found with her in a hotel near the theater district, the storm, too, expired. The clouds, like an amiable herd, trudged south, toward the hills.

Herbert Komar drove out to Grant Street that evening under a sky that was remote and hazy with faraway stars. As he climbed the Loyds' front steps the chimes from the Methodist Church broke across each other one by one: four, he counted, five, six, seven. Eight. Eight, more oblong than the others, hung suspended in the icy air like the haze of his own breath.

He crossed the porch and pressed his finger against the bell, and eight blew away, low, across the tumbled city.

"Eight?" said Blanche Loyd, listening intently as the distant last chime dissolved into silence. "Was that eight?" A streetcar passed Mamie and Clifford's house, going east toward town, and for a moment its rumble overwhelmed not only her voice but the voices of the others at Clifford and Mamie's party. "Did I miss one?" she asked Emma, when she could be heard again. "I've got half-past, and I thought I was slow."

"No, that's eight all right," said Emma. She, too, looked out the window at the tracks which, empty now, shone a little under the street lights. "Goodness!" she said. "Wouldn't you hate to put up with *that* noise all day?"

"The buses are just as bad, and they smell, too. They've put them on Grant now, you know—though I still walk up to the corner and take the streetcar. It's cheaper."

"Well," said Emma, "at least you people around here don't have to depend on a bus that runs only when it feels like it, the way Percy and I do."

She spoke with the complacency of the remote suburbanite, who knows that commutation difficulty is a sure criterion of a neighborhood's distinction.

This residential division of the old Epworth gang was now accepted (the first deserters had been regarded with a fierce amusement), but it still called forth occasional innocent remarks such as this one of Emma's. The weight of opinion, of course, had long ago shifted, and the suburbanites derived considerable pleasure from their insistence that the old neighborhood was just as nice as it had ever been. Before she and Emma descended to personalities, Blanche thought it prudent to get back to the business of the Christmas cards, which they had been transacting when the hour rang out.

She settled deeper in the chair and reached out her arms for the bulky folder of samples. "Let me see," she said. Emma, with a proud grunt at the folder's weight, lifted it up and handed it to her.

Behind them, in the dining room, there was a roar of laughter, and Frank Young shouted to his partner, "By golly, Laura, we'll scotch 'em yet!"

"Mother asked me yesterday if I'd done anything about cards," said Blanche. "It doesn't seem possible we can be so close to Christmas, does it?"

"How is Mrs. Loyd?" asked Emma. "I don't think Percy and I've seen her since spring."

"About the same," Blanche replied, leafing through the pages. "Oh, this's attractive, isn't it? No," she went on, "she's no better and no worse. Right now she's a little upset. We're talking about selling the house."

"That lovely big place? Why, Blanche, I can't picture the two of you anywhere else. Your mother won't know what to do with herself without all that room!"

"Yes," Blanche agreed, "Mother is used to a big place, but . . . Well, we'll see how it comes out. Are you selling a lot?"

"Quite a few," said Emma. "About forty dollars' worth, and I only started the last week in October."

At the dining room table Frank slapped his fist down. "*Now*, how do we stand, partner?" he trumpeted.

Blanche and Emma looked at each other.

"You'd think Lillian could hold him in, wouldn't you?" said Emma.

"If you want my opinion, I don't think she tries. That's why I begged off. You know, one game with Frank and I think my head will burst right open."

"Oh, I *know!*" agreed Emma passionately. "Don't I just know!"

So they had spoken to each other for twenty-five years, ever since Lillian married Frank and brought him into the crowd. If Frank's noisiness never subsided, neither did their interest in remarking on it. They had scarcely anything else in common.

"My!" Emma added, as the silence threatened to close in, "that lovely house . . ." and it was plain to Blanche that she was thinking complacently of the cosy apartment over the grocery store that Percy managed out in that handsome suburb.

Blanche turned another page. "This is nice," she said. " 'Wishing you,' " she read aloud, " 'at this holy season of the year, all possible joy and happiness.' "

"And," said Emma, pointing with one sharp pink nail, "if you buy two boxes you get your name printed on them free."

"Isn't *this* Christmasy!" Blanche cried, opening a card that showed a country village buried deep in snow and holly wreaths, and dotted with carollers and children on sleds:

" 'Ring in the new, ring out the old!
Christmas comes in with the snow and the cold!
Ring, jolly bells, sing, carollers gay,
A right Merry Season is coming our way!' "

But her mind countered with:

Dark, dark the deep,
And down–
Falling,
Falling . . .

What did it mean? She closed her eyes, wincing as Frank pounded the table.

"Any name up to twenty letters absolutely without charge," said Emma encouragingly.

" 'Falling, falling,' " murmured Blanche, and opened her eyes again.

"You think it over," suggested Emma. "Don't feel you have to take a box just because I'm selling them."

Blanche laughed. "Dear Emma," she said, and she felt a tender sadness for all they might have shared together, all they might have had to remember. Poor, lonely Emma, she thought. Who are you? You are a Christmas card, a grocery store, a dark little apartment; she looked at Emma's swollen legs, at the goiter that could not be cured. Falling apart, she thought, toppling down.

Emma was blushing. "Why, Blanche, you old softie! I'm just going to take those cards right away from you."

"No. Wait," said Blanche. "I'll take a box of these."

Dark, dark, and falling . . .

"Yes, the picture's pretty on that one," agreed Emma, rising and once more becoming businesslike; "but there isn't any sentiment. Look inside. I'm sure you've got the card that only says Merry Christmas and Happy New Year."

"That's all right," said Blanche. "Nobody reads the inside, anyway."

"Well, I'll be in the kitchen if you change your mind. I promised Mamie I'd help her get the lunch ready." Emma lowered her voice, though what with Frank bellowing away it was hardly necessary. "I don't think she did *one thing* before we got here! *Hon*estly!"

"Oh, I *know!*" it was Blanche's turn this time to say.

Emma glanced at her watch. "Ten after. Oh, Lord! I told her I'd be out right after that last hand. And thanks, dear, I'll get your order off first thing tomorrow."

In Grant Street Mrs. Mentone was saying, "She's been asking about you every other minute."

"I'm sorry. I thought I was right on time."

"Well, you are, but we got Blanche off to her party half an hour ago, so you could have come sooner. Last time wasn't it you got here too early? Takes practice to hit it on the button."

"Indeed it does," agreed Mr. Komar, following her into the dark kitchen. "Indeed it does."

PART FIVE

The Second Visit

· 10 ·

"Now you can relax, mother. Here he is."

"Mr. Komar?"

"Yes, Mrs. Loyd. Good evening." He took the swollen hand; her long, square nails scratched lightly over the soft flesh of his palm. In the light of the floor lamp the mottled brown skin below her knuckles looked loose and shiny, like the outer skin of an onion. He wondered whether it would crackle if he were to touch it, and whether, if he were to press a little, it would explode like a balloon, and the air come whistling out, leaving the hand hideously shrunken.

"Won't you sit down, please?" she asked pleasantly. Her eyes, with their unnerving accuracy, found out his face.

"Thank you."

"I think that chair by the window is comfortable: the rocker, I mean, by the side window." She chuckled. "The other one, by my bed, is not"—she hesitated—"is not so well suited to conversation." Her lashless, papery lids dropped across her eyes, and her expression was almost naughty. "It is more of a conversation *piece*," she said.

"Now, now, Mother," cautioned Mrs. Mentone, but in the voice of one who was accustomed to the mischief of old people, and intended only to see that it did not go too far.

Mrs. Loyd set her lips in a grim line, and one long, colorless hair in the mole beside her upper lip quivered indignantly. "Is the table cleared, Annabelle?" she asked.

"Hours ago," Mrs. Mentone replied, and sat down on the foot of Blanche's cot.

"And the pantry swept?"

"This morning."

There was a short silence. Mr. Komar set the rocker in motion, hoping that this small noise would bridge it.

"Did you empty my pot?" the old woman asked, and as she smiled slyly a dimple caught in her left cheek.

"Yes, I did," said Mrs. Mentone, "but if I hadn't I certainly wouldn't do it now."

Mrs. Loyd seemed once more to reflect.

"It's a good bit colder out," Mr. Komar observed. "I shouldn't be surprised if it went down almost to zero tonight."

He didn't realize, until too late, that he had offered Mrs. Mentone up for sacrifice.

"There, Annabelle!" exclaimed Mrs. Loyd peevishly. "I told you I was chilly. You'd better do something about that furnace."

Annabelle Mentone sighed heavily, and got to her feet.

"All right, all right," she conceded. "I'm licked. But I'm not going far. I'll be right out there in the kitchen until Lou gets home from the Elks, because if anything happens I want to know that . . . that I'm not cut off," she wound up.

Mrs. Loyd grunted scornfully. "I've stayed alone in this house all my life, and I'm not afraid to do it still. Go for a walk."

"That's right! That's right! Freeze me to death, or scare me to death: you won't care, just so I get out of here."

Mrs. Loyd made a noise halfway between a sigh and a tiny cry of frustration. Her crooked fingers played along the arm of her chair, and her jaw moved up and down as if she were chewing her gums.

Annabelle Mentone suddenly smiled. "Here," she said, stooping over the tapestry chair, "that pillow's going to break your neck." She pulled Mrs. Loyd forward a little and readjusted the bed pillow lengthwise so that it propped the old woman's back but left her neck and head free. "And look at the way you've got this blanket! No wonder you're cold."

"Thank you, Annabelle," said Mrs. Loyd gently.

"Well, I'll be in the kitchen if you want me." She paused in the doorway. "But you be good, now, Mother. I don't like all this going behind Blanche's back. If she finds out . . ." Mrs. Mentone rolled her large, eloquent eyes toward the ceiling, and her hands splayed out in the classic gesture of the betrayed woman, her shadow hugely mimicking the gesture.

"Blanche would never say a word," said Mrs. Loyd.

"That's the trouble. She'd kill me with kindness. I couldn't stand it."

"You should go back in the theater, Annabelle."

"Maybe I will, if Lou doesn't stop courting the Elks. I've got Fanny Brice's address put away somewhere. . . ." She paused again by the dining room table. "Can you stay until nine-thirty, Mr. Komar? Lou promised he'd be home early tonight."

Mr. Komar hesitated. "Why . . ." he glanced at Mrs. Loyd, and, as he had expected, her blank eyes were on him again.

"I hope you will," Mrs. Loyd said. "Annabelle is frightened to be alone in the house with me."

"That's right," retorted Mrs. Mentone, as she passed into the kitchen, "maybe it *is* you and not the house at all!"

Mrs. Loyd snorted derisively.

When they were alone, her eyes did not move from his face. Mr. Komar shifted nervously in his rocker. In desperation, he said, "Does he really exist?"

"Exist? Who?"

"Mr. Mentone. I keep hearing about him, but . . ."

"He exists."

"Well, it was a foolish question."

"He exists," the old woman pursued; "I would not say that he lives. His claim to our attention is that his family home in the city is now a funeral parlor. He has found his distinction in having lost—everything. Does that seem an accomplishment to you, Mr. Komar?"

"An accomplishment, perhaps."

"Yes, I daresay it is. My daughter seems intent on the same kind of distinction. As you will understand now, she knows nothing of your visit tonight."

"I guessed that when I talked to Mrs. Mentone on Friday. A party?"

"Yes, she's at a party."

"I wondered how you knew my number at home?"

"My daughter is a methodical woman. She has you down in that pad there, beside the telephone." Mrs. Loyd's mouth twisted bitterly. "She knows it could be painted on a sign and hung over my bed, for all I would know of it."

"She has been honest with you."

"Honest! As if anything were ever clearer for honesty!"

"Would you have liked it better if she'd gone ahead without telling you what she was doing?"

"She could not." Mrs. Loyd grunted again, and her jaw moved ferociously. "Oh, she could have, I suppose; but"—she smiled—"I would have died from the shock. Murder. She'd never have forgiven herself. Blanche has a tender conscience. I rather think her conscience is responsible for this present impasse. And, because she will go on being what she is, we may expect matters to get worse quite soon. Her sort of honesty and kindness do kill, as Annabelle said. I am hard, Mr. Komar," she went on, her eyes meeting his directly; "hard, and they tell me I am domineering, too. I make up my mind. I may change it a thousand times, but I would rather do that than be afraid ever to act on what I thought was right. You may hate me, Mr. Komar, but you will not need to be afraid of me. We will understand each other."

"And, your daughter? . . ."

"She is too tender, too kind, too honest. She throws the burden on all of us equally, on you, on me, on my sons: then she waits."

"I think you underestimate her."

"I think not. Rather, she overestimates me, my resistance. I am old, Mr. Komar, really old. I am obliged to go on living: I come from a hardy family. You must not count on my dying soon enough to solve this problem for all of you. Blanche depends on my doing one of two things, either dying from resisting you or resisting you and saving her. I can not, as I say, guarantee the first. As for the second: there she banks too much. I am too tired to fight you, Mr. Komar. I have no resources, either. I can only ask you to let me alone, and to make my daughter let you alone."

"You don't want to sell the house?"

"I do not. But you know that, have known it from the first. Let me ask whether you think my daughter wants to sell?"

"She says it will have to be sold."

"Ah! Her admirable honesty again. Has she mentioned a price to you?"

"We have agreed on that."

"I'm sure you are very generous."

"It's a fair price: more than fair, she says, for the house needs a good deal of repair."

"What splendid candor! She made this plain at once?"

"Yes, at our first meeting."

"And, did the state of repairs make you hesitate?"

"A little, I think, until I came out here."

"And she has said, in plain words, that this house is for sale?"

He hesitated. "I thought so—when I went to see her at her office."

"Has she spoken frankly since then?"

"Oh, very frankly. She's told me all that you and she said to each other after my visit last Monday."

"I'm sure she has. And it is your understanding that I am all that stands between you and the house?"

"Yes," he said bluntly.

For a moment Mrs. Loyd's restless hands were still. She closed her eyes and leaned her head against the chair back. The light from the floor lamp struck mercilessly across her face, and she looked tired: tired enough, he thought, really to die at once.

"Perhaps that's right," she said. She lifted one hand until it shaded her eyes, but she did not open them. "But I doubt it. And I think Blanche doubts it, too. And—you?"

"I have given you my understanding."

"Yes, you have to cling to that, don't you? Otherwise, the whole transaction is a comedy." She may have sensed his confusion, for she added, "If Blanche does not want to sell, either, then you are . . ." She broke off out of what was perhaps mistaken kindness. But he now understood her.

"Superfluous," he finished. "You're right, of course. That way it would be a comedy: and cruel."

"And cruel," she agreed. "And Blanche is so kind."

In the street an automobile sounded its horn, and then its headlights struck against the side window as it drove up the next-door driveway. The clock on the mantel chimed the three-quarter hour.

"Before nine or ten?" she asked.

"Before nine."

"I feel as if we had been talking a great while. Would you like a cup of coffee, Mr. Komar?"

"That would be very nice."

"I generally have one about this time. It does not seem to keep me awake after they've put me to bed, as a later cup does." Her hands disappeared under the blanket. He judged that they were grasping a cane that lay between her legs, for there followed three raps against the floor. "These little rituals," she said, extracting her hands again. "How reassuring they are. Sometimes, when I have had a hard day—my heart is bad, you know: it's not an invalid's trick—sometimes, then, I take my cup of coffee, and I think it could all be so much worse, and I say to myself that it must be about nine o'clock now, and that I shall soon be asleep. I begin to feel almost—almost like a human being again. I am not somebody's mother, somebody's widow: I am myself. I am Lily Loyd. I wish you could have seen me when I had my looks. They tell me that I was very beautiful. And the men—I could have had the pick of Yarmouth, Mr. Komar. But I married—I thought that I married for love." She smiled. He saw that although her lips were narrow now, she had a generous mouth. "Poor Jerry!" she murmured tenderly. "The price of age is to learn how much is forgotten; how little really matters. I have thought my heart was broken a thousand times, but now I can not even remember what I grieved for. I think there is a romantic notion that men and women die a little at a time—die whenever they lose someone or something that they love. That is a heady idea, and admirably suited to youth. Age teaches one that what finally kills is boredom. I know now that a cup of coffee at nine o'clock in the evening is far more dependable than first love, and in the end a greater comfort, but the price has been too dear: to know the meaning of everything is to know that what one embraces is nothing. I was beautiful once, and I died a thousand times with passion, and now I am old and intolerably bored. The nights are my blessing, for in them I return to that part of myself that will not accept fact. You would be surprised at what I dream sometimes. I am running barefoot through grass, or I am gripping the headboard of my bed and the doctor is pulling the red, silent baby from between my legs, and I cry out . . . and Blanche touches my shoulder and says, 'Mother, you were having a nightmare.' *Nightmare* . . . Could I tell her what joy I felt, how that pain was I, Lily Loyd? I turn my head on the dry pillow, I, an old lady in a cold bed, and blind, and say, 'Oh, thank you, Blanche.' Yes, I pay dearly. To know is to die in life." She moved a little in her chair, trying to straighten herself: a futile attempt; but he was too kind to offer help. "It is the days," she said tiredly, "the days that take so much time to get through. In them I am the recipient of God's ironic grace. And where is that woman?" she asked impatiently. "Mr. Komar, would you mind telling her that I want my coffee?"

But just as he was getting to his feet, Mrs. Mentone came out of the kitchen bearing a tray with cups on it, and a coffee pot.

"I knew what you were after," she said, entering the room.

"It's fresh, too. Mr. Komar, will you take those books off the end table for me? . . . Thank you." She lowered the tray, and put two cups on their saucers.

"Won't you have some?" asked Mr. Komar.

"Mine's on the kitchen table. The help has to keep its place, you know."

"I wish the help would hold that in mind a little more often," said Mrs. Loyd.

"You keep a civil tongue, old lady," replied Mrs. Mentone amiably. "And just for that, you can drink it without cream. We've got to strip you down somehow."

"I'm past the stripping point," said Mrs. Loyd, and she giggled.

"None of that, now. There's a gentleman present."

"There wouldn't be much point if–"

"Ah! for shame!" cried Mrs. Mentone. Mr. Komar had blushed, and slopped coffee into his saucer. "He's as red as a barn. Where's your modesty?"

"I lost it the day–"

"Here, here, now! What would Blanche think of this?"

"I was going to say," replied Mrs. Loyd composedly, "that I lost it the day Blanche bought me my conversation piece."

"Yes you were!" jeered Mrs. Mentone. She spread a dish towel across Mrs. Loyd's lap, and gave her the cup of coffee. "Now, don't spill it. Mr. Komar, will you put her cup back on the tray when she's finished? The rest she can manage herself. She'll probably want more. I can't fill it very full for fear she'll tip it down the front of her."

"I may be blind and helpless," snapped Mrs. Loyd, "but as yet I am not stone deaf."

"Then that's the only ailment you don't claim."

"At least I don't go around the house whining about my change of–"

"You and your dirty mind!" said Mrs. Mentone hastily. "Shame on you. And here I made you a fresh pot. Where's your gratitude?"

"Where my modesty is."

"I'll hear no more of this!" said Mrs. Mentone; and she left the room with dignified haste. She avoided looking at Mr. Komar.

"She's a good sort, for one of her class," said Mrs. Loyd, without even attempting to lower her voice.

"I heard that!" shouted Mrs. Mentone from the kitchen. "And I'm every bit as good as you are!"

"Yes, and I'll bet you've heard everything else," retorted Mrs. Loyd.

There was no reply, but a pan, perhaps, or the kettle, crashed against the stove.

"Noisy," commented Mrs. Loyd, "and saddled with a husband who's never done a man's job in his life."

"Listen," said Mrs. Mentone, "you should get in bed with him once!"

Both ladies laughed: Mrs. Mentone's high-pitched, genteel scream was perfectly audible in the living room.

The mantel clock struck nine, and Mr. Komar, looking toward it, saw again the photograph in the silver frame.

"Whose picture is that?" he asked, and then, remembering that his hostess was blind, added, "On the mantel. I can't see it the way the light is."

"That? I suppose it's the picture of me. There used to be one there."

"May I look at it?" He put his cup back on the tray and got up. As he crossed the rug he was reminded of that first visit, exactly one week ago, and of how the old woman had wakened and arrested his intention. He looked at her, and her eyes were on him, moving as he moved across the room. He took up the heavy frame.

There were the eyes again, but not opaque; rather, bottomless, and brilliant; cold, and, in the black-and-white photograph, dark. The eyebrows gave the face its look of inquiry; the nose and the height of forehead added arrogance; and the mouth: was she smiling? He looked at the original: Lily Loyd still seemed to be watching him, and there was amusement in her face, and inquiry . . . but the poor eyes were fires gone out.

"Did he make a joke?" he asked.

"Who?"

"The photographer. You look . . . about to laugh; or to say something?"

"I can't remember. That was twenty years ago–soon after the war ended, I think. It was a dark little shop in one of the downtown arcades: I remember that. And the day–it must have been this time of year, for I know that my ears were red with cold. I wondered how they would look in the picture. Perhaps that is why I was laughing."

"It's a good picture."

"Yes, I know that I always liked it. I suppose I think of myself that way still, with my lace collar, and the pearls–my son Covil gave them to me when he got his first job. I don't know which of us was prouder. And here I sit: buried in blankets and pillows, covered with a dish towel, not allowed even to hold a full cup of coffee."

"You are not so greatly changed," he answered, putting the photograph back.

"The eyes . . ."

"Yes; those, of course. Still . . ."

"Ah, you are determined to be kind," she said, but without protest, and she smiled at him.

"Can I bring you more coffee?–A full cup," he added.

"Please. But not too full. Annabelle is right: I do spill it down the front of me. And a little cream, I think."

"Your eyes are blue," he said, bending over her as she reached uncertainly for the saucer; and perhaps there was surprise in his voice.

Quickly, her lids came down. "Do the cataracts cover so much, then, that you are not sure?"

"Not that. I'd never looked before, I think; in your photograph they look black as jets."

"To be told that my eyes are blue . . . how you rock my composure!"

"But you are determined to be firm?"

"Yes, to be firm."

"About the house?"

"I was not thinking of the house; but, yes, about that, too."

"We have got a long way from it."

"Not so far, perhaps. Why do you want my house, Mr. Komar?"

"I want a home. It's now, I think, if I'm ever to do it. I'm sixty."

"But . . . *my* house? You must know that there are many other large places—even on this street—that could be bought. In the time you have spent coming here and seeing my daughter (yes, she told me of your luncheon), I believe, though I don't know much of these things, that you could have found some other place and settled most of the details of buying it."

"I suppose so," he answered.

"Then, why do you give yourself—I will not talk of my part in it, or Blanche's—so much needless trouble? You don't impress me as a man who acts stubbornly to opposition. Am I correct in thinking that ordinarily, when your way is blocked, you turn off in another direction—almost without thinking?"

"Ordinarily," he agreed. "But"—and he thought of his drive home on Friday night, of Mrs. Hlavaty's offended dignity, of his loneliness; even, he thought of Mary Bush, and, thinking, raised his eyes to her portrait—"but," he said, "now I have no other way to take. I have"—he groped for his meaning—"I have followed all the routes of compromise, and they've led me in a circle. I'm back where I started, and no wiser." He hesitated. "*She'd* know," he said, half desperately.

"My daughter?"

"Your daughter!" he echoed, astonished. "I mean, Mary Bush. . . . What is it she does with her hands? I can't see. The light falls across the canvas."

"Shut it off," she directed, and waited as he stood over her examining the cracked painting.

"Was that a veil?" he asked. "And for whom?"

"I don't know. She sewed a great deal, and beautifully, too. The convent training, I suppose."

"She watches you," he said; "the you on the mantel."

"Or I, her?" she asked, rather grimly.

"No. The other way. Did she care about her house?"

"She ran it well. Help was cheap then. She didn't do much herself. She was always out and gone. But, yes, in her way she loved it."

"Not in your way," he suggested, pulling her light on again and going back to his chair; for, after all, the painting was too much of a reality: the Mary Bush of sunlit fields, of arms reaching up, belonged in his mind; the lady in the portrait was dead.

"I don't love this house," Mrs. Loyd answered. "I value it. But you're right in what you say. Mary had—other things."

"And you?"

"I have only my nights . . . and this house. Tell me why you think she would understand."

"I think she would laugh at my wanting this or any house so much, but she'd say I was right not, for once, to take an easier way."

"She was hard on herself," agreed Mrs. Loyd, "and on others."

"As hard as you?" he asked, smiling.

"Yes, I told you I was hard, didn't I? To be hard, and hard on others: possibly they are the same in the end. But my hardness is a new thing, born of resignation. Mary was never resigned, even at the end. I remember . . . I remember one day: it must have been in Ninety-six, for she died that year. She had grown very ill. She scarcely left the house any more. She sat in that rocker—the very one you are in—and sewed endlessly. I can see her needle catching the sun, and she must have pricked her finger, I think, for I remember she hurled the quilt on the floor, and got up and stamped her foot on it. The temper she had! My husband picked up the quilt and gave it to her, and suddenly she laughed like a girl and went on as if nothing had happened. But there were little drops of blood across the squares of cloth, and her face!— I remember that moment so clearly, the two of them together in the light, so much alike in their passion, though they were no blood kin, of course . . . I remember. And both of them dead hardly more than a year later, and the house mine—to dispose of."

She held out her empty cup to him, and he got up and put it back on the tray.

"You don't tell me," she went on, "why choosing some other house than this one would be out of the question. Have you tried before, and failed?"

"This is the first house I've ever looked at. I have talked about buying one for years, and done nothing. Then, the week before last, one of the men in my office told me that this house might be for sale, and might just suit me. He has insurance with Miss Loyd. So, I called her and then went to see her."

"Frankly, I don't understand. You've not even been over it, have you?"

"No . . ."

"We might, you know, simply be very clever salesmen. The roof may be falling off, the plumbing obsolete (it is), the floors in need of shoring. . . . Surely it would be no compromise on your part to want to see over the house you're offering money for?"

"No . . ." he said once again, for he did not know how to tell her that all these considerations, while ultimately affecting his actual purchase of the house, did not affect his first desiring simply to get her consent. "What do you think of me?" he asked suddenly.

"I?" She appeared surprised. "I think you want to take my house away."

"Now you are being honest after your daughter's fashion."

She was silent a moment. "I think nothing of you," she presently answered.

Here was the crux, and he felt fear pulling slack the muscles in his thighs and wrists. "Of me? Or, about me?"

The mantel clock struck nine-thirty, and through the strokes of the tiny clapper, as impersonal and remote as the chimes that rang out, he heard her voice saying, "I can't answer now without telling you more than I might later mean, or less."

The machinery shut itself off, and in the heavy silence he moved restlessly in his chair. He looked at the portrait, and the blue, blue eyes were turned away from him, unaware of him. . . .

"That's it," he said quietly, as if he were responding to all that Lily Loyd might have told him; "you . . . forget me, you and your daughter both. I am only a kind of buffer between you. What game," he said with an abrupt fierceness, "are the two of you playing? What has it to do with me? You talk about Blanche's peculiar kind of honesty, but is it really so much different from your own? I think you are hard, and domineering—and I know now that you are infinitely more subtle than she. You didn't bring me here tonight for a frank talk. Tonight is another move; you think to block her. But I am no counter, nor any buffer. I don't know the name of this game; I don't even know the stakes you're playing for. But I know the game that *I'm* playing, and I warn you, Mrs. Loyd, I warn you to remember *me*. . . ."

His voice had gradually risen with intensity, and now he stopped, for its tremors were painfully apparent.

"To remember *you*," she echoed scornfully. Her fingers clutched and unclutched in the folds of her blanket. "I've tried. I've given you this evening to show me you deserve it. Poor, lonely man! Poor . . . cipher!"

He felt the blood draining from his face in his anger. "You Loyds—you proud Loyds!" he said, struggling desperately to keep his voice clear. "And I give you all credit for it. You're so much above the mob that you can cut them to pieces and say they're better for it: their wounds make them aware of themselves, even if they die for the knowledge. And I'm mob, wound, buffer, counter . . ."—his voice broke, half in laughter, half with tears—"it's wonderful how much I can be and be nothing!"

"If you expect me to weep for you, you are sadly wrong." She spoke so coldly, so steadily, that an almost wonderful thrill of horror struck through him. "I weep for no one: each man makes his bed, and he can die in it for all of me. The poor are poor because they deserve no better, and the starving—let them starve; and the mob—let them be ridden across. Mankind is stupid; ah God! how stupid. Life is what you will to make of it, and fate is nothing more than cunning and bravery. Why should I scruple to use you when you give yourself to me . . ."

"In trust," he interrupted fiercely.

"In blindness. No, I do not pity you. *Fight* me!" she cried, with a terrible passion, "fight me and I'll love you . . . *cipher*."

"You have all the weapons," he replied. "Blind, old, sick, poor—"

"Enough!"

"I'll fight!" he shouted, jumping to his feet. "You poor blind woman, I'll fight you to death!"

Lily Loyd gave a strangled cry, but whether of rage or exaltation he did not know. She pounded the floor with her cane, and Mrs. Mentone came running in, her usually florid face white and grave.

She sent him an angry glance, and demanded, "What's going on in here?"

"Show him the house!" commanded Mrs. Loyd.

Mrs. Mentone's astonishment was ludicrous. "Do what?"

"*Show him the house!* Every crumbling brick, every spider. But get him out of my room! Get out!"

They retreated toward the dining room. Mrs. Mentone's hand rested against one of his arms, but whether for protection or to see that he obeyed neither of them could have said. The old woman's blank, white eyes looked straight ahead; they might already have gone, for any notice she took of them. But as they passed into the kitchen, she called, "Show him the basement," and terrible and desolate in the still house was the sound of her wrenching laughter.

· 11 ·

"I'LL GO."

"Please, don't."

"But this . . . *comedy!*" he protested.

"Go through with it. If you don't, I'm the one who'll pay." Annabelle Mentone's thick shoulders slumped inside her bright, loose housedress, and her fleshy face looked haggard and frightened. "Christ," she murmured, "what you've brought me to!" He thought she addressed some more concrete presence than the Son, but she seemed not to be thinking of himself. "To get out of here," she said despairingly. "Doesn't he think of me?"

An alarm clock on the shelf over the sink galloped metallically; she glanced toward it. "Quarter of ten; and he *promised*. . . ." She shrugged, and a tremor passed through her heavy body. "It's terrible to be poor," she whispered. "She's not like Blanche, who'll stick little knives in you, day and night; but I think she's almost worse. She gets angry just as quickly, and stays angry just as long; and she'll batter you to death—not because you're you (she's quite fond of me, really), but because you mean less than her rage, and she must have her satisfaction."

"She told me she was too tired to fight," he remembered wonderingly.

"She's tired, but she'll fight. She was so strong once that now she seems to herself weaker than she really is."

"You're fond of her?"

"I'm a fool about people—have been all my life. When she's in a good humor—you saw what she can be like—I forget the rest of her. I remember she's blind, and so damned helpless. And"—

she shrugged again with an attempt at jauntiness—"I remember I have to have a place to live." She looked down at her clenched hands, and absent-mindedly picked flakes of bright red polish off a thumbnail. "I make all my big mistakes about men," she went on, but without bitterness. "In some ways she's so like a man, too—I feel the same stupid happiness when I please her; and the same sickness when she chews me up. To live with her: it's like a long love affair, so passionate that you know it'll end in—death."

The word, so present during that evening, seemed to add its own weight and density to the stifling atmosphere. He felt again that he was drowning in large questions and irrevocable decisions that no one would tell him about, that he could not answer himself.

"I should be over love at my time of life, shouldn't I?" she asked. "A fat slob like me?"

"Oh, I don't know," he said; and meant it—he who had given all that up so many years ago, almost before it had begun. "You can't be very old."

"I'm fifty-two," she told him; "and I know it . . . and Lou knows it. I married him eight years ago, and I thought . . . I can't even remember now what I did think. It's funny how all your hopes blow up, isn't it, and only your fear is always with you?"

"Yes, it finally gets you."

"It's got *her*," she said, with a nod toward the living room. "But it's her strength. Hope . . . she'd hate being able to hope; you don't want to fight something like that." She now, for the first time, looked at him directly. "Well . . ." she said, and her hands splayed out once more in that gesture of betrayal; but this time it had no value as comedy: in the very modification which she unconsciously gave it he sensed truth; and because they were both, in their ways, the betrayed, he had the courage to say.

"The Elks?"

She turned away from him and went toward the pantry door. "We call it the Elks. He's six years younger than I am. . . . This is the pantry." She pulled the string on the overhead light, and the rectangular brown room sprang into clarity. "Lots of cupboards, though those glass doors are hell to keep clean." She crossed to the further end and opened a tin-lined bin that was disguised on the outside as a row of drawers. "For flour," she said. "Actually, you could put storage closets out in the kitchen and the back hall, and turn this into a bathroom. You want to break the place up into flats, or something, don't you?"

"Yes. I'd keep the first floor for myself, however."

She preceded him out of the room. "And the kitchen again," she said.

"Large."

"Like an ice rink. This door leads to the back hall." She pushed it open, and they stood in a rush of cold air. "Refrigerator." She pointed. "Fruit bins, mop, Bissel, pail; also, convenient for storing old newspapers—and garbage if you don't want to go out in the cold and put it in the can."

"Where does this lead?"

He touched the panels that were immediately to his right, at right angles with the outside door.

"It gives on the back stairs." She turned the knob. "We might as well go up this way, now we're out here."

They climbed the perilous steep flight, guided by an unshaded bulb that hung over the landing at the top. The hand rail was icy cold to his touch, and like all back stairways this one was so damp that one might have been climbing an earthen tunnel whose walls had become cascades for the winter spill of melting snow. Mrs. Mentone's heavy tread shook the risers, and their joint steps raised a deafening clatter. He wanted to go lightly, quietly, but a silent progress was impossible on the bare, hollow boards. He began to understand some of the housekeeper's insecurity when she was alone in these expanses of shadow and cold.

Here, in this precipitous tunnel, one was trapped, and the expectation that beyond the circle of light far ahead lay something dark, formless—something that *flopped,* he thought unexpectedly —this expectation could hardly be put down.

They reached the top, and Mrs. Mentone paused, breathing heavily. He looked back into almost complete blackness, for their shadows blotted up the dim fall of light.

The woman followed his gaze. "I'd block this off," she said vehemently. "To sit down there and know that—that you can be got at either from the front or back . . . it's terrible. The noises in an old house at night! How can they all be due to settlings?" She shivered; he saw the flesh on her bare arms standing out in bumps. "The past closes around me in this place. When I was a little girl I used to dream that a fiery red ball bounced up the front stairs in our house, and somehow, lying in my bed, I could see it skipping—so lightly, and yet it had an awful weight to it—along the hall to my room. And then"—her voice diminished as the ancient fear caught at her—"and then it would shrink and shrink and slide under my door, and while I watched it grew large again, and larger, and slowly it pushed itself toward me. I could hear its heavy breathing, and I would sit up in bed and scream; and then, gradually, the light would sink out of the room, and I'd find myself wound in the bedclothes, sitting in the cold and in absolute darkness." She paused again, her breath more labored by the effort she had made to be clear. "I've never forgotten that dream. The ball didn't reach me in those days, but I know that if it had . . ." Her voice trembled and died. "Now, it's found me again; but it's clever. It doesn't come when I'm in bed, with Lou beside me to be turned to;—no, it comes when I sit alone, with the lights on and the gas popping in the fireplace. I hear that ball . . . thud, it goes, thud . . . coming down these back stairs, flopping down them, as if it has to learn a new way to travel in its old age and mine." She looked at him as she opened the door into the hall and passed through. "Do you think the dead can come back?" she asked, with such seriousness that the question did not strike him as absurd, or even embarrassing.

"Only through the living," he replied.

"I believe," she said fervently. "I've seen . . . strange sights: doors that swung and latched when no one touched them; a Bible once that fell off a table in the middle of the night; I've heard voices call my name when I knew I was alone, and so clear have they been that I've got up, saying 'Yes?', because I thought that someone had come home without my hearing."

"In the mind," he said gently.

"In the mind!" she sneered. "What fine things science has done. It takes away one set of beliefs and gives us another; and it is so scrupulous that it tells us these new ones, too, may be fictions, and that we must not count on them; and yet, with a perfectly straight face, it assures us that the old beliefs are foolish and unfounded, because you can't mix them in a test tube, or build a machine to produce them. It hates the secret of life, and so it goes on from where life begins. But I"—she hesitated—"I"—she laughed uncertainly and switched on the light in a tiny rear bedroom—"I trust the senses."

They stepped into the room. It contained a double brass bed, a chest of drawers painted light green, a straw-bottomed rocker, and a bookcase. There was only one decoration on the wall: an enormous family group roosting in a gilt frame whose plaster scallops were here and there chipped or broken.

"The relatives," said Mrs. Mentone. "There's the gal in the painting downstairs."

He stepped closer. "Which one?" he asked, and as she crossed the room to straighten the shade at the window, "Which one?" he demanded.

"Right square in the middle. The one sitting down."

Ah, God! he thought, it could not be. That fat, tiny woman in voluminous black, with—was it?—a lace cap over her hair, and an invalid's face, round, shining, devoid of any expression.

"Why," he cried, stricken, "she *does* look . . ."

"Doesn't she?" agreed Mrs. Mentone. "Except that the one downstairs has about forty years on her, and weighs *two* tons."

"Well . . ." he said, with a shaken laugh.

"Regular hellers, both of them," Mrs. Mentone remarked.

He would not dispute the statement; and he turned away, glad that the lady of his dreams was to some extent dissociated from her portrait. But which, he wondered, as the light was flicked out and they stepped back into the hall, which was the real Mary Bush?

"The Irish have a way of shrinking," remarked Mrs. Mentone academically. "Bathroom," she said. "Just like any other, but the tub stands on legs, and it takes hours for all the water to run out. Did you ever notice that? About the Irish, I mean. Take quite a big one: he'll be down to nothing at seventy. Now, the English," she went on, with a pride that, he assumed, she justified by being herself of that descent, "you can't stop 'em. Start little bits of things, but Lord! how they mushroom out! And a good thing. No man wants to crawl in bed with a stick; nor any woman, either. That's the thing about the English. They're cosy."

"I never thought of them as a very cosy people," he objected, peering into another, larger bedroom, vast and apparently untenanted, for there were no brushes on the dressing table, no slippers under the chair.

"Well, but you aren't English," she pointed out. His face must have worn a curious expression, for she added, "Nothing personal, you know. I mean, you aren't, are you?"

"No," he replied; and then, fearing he had sounded too short, added, "Something just moved in my mind. I know you meant nothing, but I wonder—does *she?*"

"You'd have to ask her."

"She'd never tell me."

"She would, if she were sure," Mrs. Mentone said. "Blanche wouldn't—ever. And in trying to guess what she really thought you might be right and you might not."

"If it matters," he went on (the lights in the Mentones' big bedroom and in a room used now apparently for storage were flicked on, flicked off, but he scarcely noticed), "why does she want me to see the house?"

"She's not finished with you yet," said Mrs. Mentone.

"Nor I with her," he answered grimly. "Whose room is this?"

They stood in the fifth bedroom, at the head of the front stairway.

She did not answer, but waited expectantly. It looked to be a room often retreated to but not much lived in: the disposal place of mementos kept austerely neat. It was a woman's room, a woman's history, a room of the mind. It said everything, but, in a way, obliquely, so that the contents did not each time add up to the same total. On the bed, sprawling with an erotic abandon, was a doll dressed in skirt on skirt of pink tulle. It had a bone-white china face, and enormous brown eyes, staring, insistent, mindless. The mouth was small, deeply indented, and of a peculiar bluish-red, as if in its ecstasy it had frozen to death. Brittle, dark hair lay stiffly against the blue coverlet, and the white face glistened as if with grave-damp. A corpse, he concluded with sudden horror, struck dead in the very self-destroying act of love.

"I love these old dolls," said Mrs. Mentone, picking it up and fondling the pretty skirts. "Hasn't she got a wicked look? Oh, naughty lady! what you could tell." Then she set the doll back against the pillows and said wryly, "Nothing; that's all she'd have to tell, spending her days in this room." She looked around. "Clutter, clutter," she said. "What's she want with all this stuff? It takes me hours to dust." She picked up a tiny child in Royal Doulton, all white and dusty gray, that stood on the night table beside the enormous bed. "If I've washed this once, I've done it a thousand times, and I know one day I'm going to drop it."

But he did not hear her. He was looking toward the far wall of the room, where a great oval looking glass leaned in its vaulting frame over a low mahogany dressing table. An electric bulb in a pink silk shade hung from the ceiling directly in front of the glass, to light the lady as she painted and powdered and fixed on her brilliant sunburst, as she drew out the dagger-sharp stopper on the blue-glass bottle and touched the perfume lightly—here, behind the ears, here, in the soft hollow of the throat. A yellowing silver case stood open, he saw as he drew closer, and out of its sandalwood interior tumbled a glittering necklace of black and gold: only jets, he saw, and the gold perhaps not real, but what romance they claimed for themselves! A single pendant earring sprawled on the shining wood: silver and ice perishably joined. In the depths of the box he caught sudden, shifting gleams and flashes from stones of glassy green, arrogant and cheaply proud; from garnets that burned with a somber fire; from pearl earrings so big they were a travesty of the oyster's patient work.

Along the edge of the dressing table lay a spill of powder, richly pink, more evocative than he had ever found a woman's flesh. He caught his breath. Almost, it was a forbidden sight, cruel in its unawareness.

He looked down. On the rug lay the other earring. The lady had left in a hurry, and what a pity she had descended to a Chevrolet or a Ford. She should have been lit down the stairway by candles that made her eyes bright and secretive; her skirts should have whispered against the banisters; and she should have gone out to a coach that, dark and sullen, had carried her off to . . . to what? To something wicked, wicked.

From where he stood he could see himself completely in the looking glass. He wondered how often she had stood thus, the dark room reflected behind her, advancing toward the light, sitting down on the pretty bench to brush the girl's hair, to powder the woman's cheeks, to rouge and paint the spinster's face. How often had the swinging crystals been clamped on the rosy lobes, the rope of garnets slung round the thickening neck, the powder strewn and dusted off, the doll moved, the bedspread pulled back over the foot? And all for nothing, he thought wearily; nothing at all, he saw, looking around the room. For elsewhere the promise of luxuriant femininity was buried under the refuse of a woman's growing solitary years: all the impedimenta of living, but only beneath the great looking glass, the impedimenta of life.

". . . are you?" asked Mrs. Mentone, and he had the impression she had been talking for some time.

"I'm sorry; I'm afraid I wasn't listening."

"I said that if I were Blanche I'd clear a lot of this junk out. What's the use of keeping so much stuff? Somebody just has to go through it and dump it after you die. And who wants to be reminded of the past all the time? God knows you carry enough of it around with you. I asked you if you felt that way?"

He laughed, and the man in the oval glass travestied the expression, turning it into a grimace. "I have no past." If this gently pink and gray, this crowded room, expressed its mistress' tragic complication, it served to point up even more strongly to him his own poverty and desolating simplicity.

"All set?" There was mild reproach in her voice. "Or do you want to look under the bed, too?"

"All set," he answered, and picked his way through tables and chairs, past bed and bookcase, to the door.

They started down the front stairway. Blocking off the landing were dark green velvet portières, double-faced.

"Draft curtains," said Mrs. Mentone, lifting one aside. "We just got them up yesterday." She sighed. "One more thing to worry about," she said, as they emerged on the landing. "They've got a way of billowing out. You never know what's on the other side. Though," she added, with an effort at fairness, "I must admit that it's never tried to get down the front way. The only thing is"—the portière dropped silently into place—"will these give it ideas?"

"You're not trying to discourage me about this house, too?"

"I? God forbid! The haunters will probably go out with the haunted. In the mind, you said? Well, maybe so."

"Let me see: a red ball on the second floor, Dracula in the attic, and a nameless something behind the furnace."

"Now you're laughing. You wait. If these go, something of yours will come in their place."

"But, I told you, I have no past."

"That's all the worse," she told him solemnly. "You'll find one here."

He swung away from her impatiently, toward the wall that faced down the stairway, and there, hanging on the faded brown field of daisies, almost like a spectre flung abruptly up to confute him and justify Annabelle Mentone's warning, was a framed drawing of the rural seat. He did not at once notice the artist's signature and the date in the corner, but it was apparent that the drawing was old. Dust had filtered inside the cheap, painted frame and lay in undulations across the yellowing paper of the drawing itself. The paper was so thin that almost he could see the thin cardboard backing. The house tilted a little to one side—the result, it might be, of inexpert but painstaking attention to perspective, and was drawn so as to show its disjunctive façade and one of the massive end chimneys. The windows were absurdly too small, and the overzealous attempt to indicate the clapboard siding made the walls look as if they were composed of ruled sheets of tablet paper. The shadows of trees, fence posts, of the house itself, fell at random from a scattered sun. Someone—a woman—stood in one of the three doorways: a stiff little figure without dimension or life. Yet, the drawing—apparently made with a pen with a splintered nib—was peculiarly arresting in a way that the exact reproduction of the rural seat in Blanche Loyd's office was not: the house seemed here, with its perilous tilt, its cosmic shadows, to have been fixed in a disruptive moment in time, fixed forever in its not-quite-truthfulness, a house in a snowstorm ball that had been dropped and shaken and cracked.

He leaned closer. "Miss Lizzie Loyd," he read, "Yarmouth, 1848."

"If that were built of stone," remarked Mrs. Mentone, "I'd say it was the place whoever wrote *Wuthering Heights* had in mind. But you don't dare tell that to *them*. To hear 'em talk they haven't known a day's quiet since they got away from the place. What'd they ever leave it for? A happy rural seat," she said. "They can have it. Give me the city any time."

"It must have seemed like a haven to Mary Bush," he murmured reflectively.

"Maybe so. Everybody to their taste. You got some kind of bug in your bonnet about her?"

He had a desire to answer her honestly and yet not fully, and presently he said, "It's the nosiness of an old bachelor who has no Mary Bush in his family, I suppose; who doesn't even know the name of his great-grandfather."

"Well, as to that, I don't know the name of mine, either. But I know what you mean."

"It's something to be proud of, don't you think?" he went on, looking down to watch his footing on the steps. "–To feel that strong, clear tie with so many pasts."

"The past again! Listen, tell me what it's ever got them? Here they are, two old women, and stiff-necked as hell."

"Yes, I've thought that too, and yet . . . well, I don't know."

"And you can't tell me," she continued, "that these Jeremiahs and what's-her-names were anything like *this* pair, either. Oh, these two have guts, don't mistake me there; they're like the others as far as that goes. But something's missing now. I've tried to figure it out. The fire's gone. You know what I mean. I don't think the old Loyds were ever rich, but they were somebody. Now the Loyds are somebody only among themselves, the way everyone else is; and that," she added vulgarly, "kills them."

"I don't know," he said again, and in silence they went down the last few steps to the front hall.

"Parlor over here," said Mrs. Mentone, "but you've seen that. I'll put on the light, and you can take a quick look at the basement."

"I've seen enough. It's getting late, and I've got to be up early."

He walked over to the great, ornate rack and took down his coat. "I'll be getting along. Thank you."

"Wait a minute. I'll see if there're any last words"—and she indicated the sliding door beyond which Lily Loyd was sitting.

"I don't think we have more to say to each other," he replied stiffly.

"Well, wait for my sake." She dropped her voice still lower, though they had been speaking in diminished tones ever since they passed beyond the portières. "I'll get the devil if you just go off."

He nodded, and she went swiftly into the kitchen. A moment later he heard a murmur of voices in the living room, and then Mrs. Mentone was back in the hall once more.

"She'd like to see you—just briefly. She says that what she wants to tell you ought to please you very much."

· 12 ·

LILY Loyd's forehead rested against one of her hands, and she did not open her eyes as he approached. The lamp caught the fine down along her cheeks, and shivered across the single hair that dropped from the mole at the corner of her lips.

"You've seen my house?"

"Enough of it."

"And your offer still holds?"

"It does," he replied steadily.

She moved a little. "If I can get myself forward, will you do something with this pillow?" He leaned over her as slowly, grasping the arms of the chair, she inched herself upright. "Push it down. Yes, that feels all right. Thank you." She must have heard his motion backward, toward the fireplace, for she said, "Wait. Give me your hand."

Her palms were dry and warm, his own right hand clapped between them: bony and slippery and cold.

"This is a smooth hand." Her fingers explored it slowly, yet without hesitation. "Are you warm enough?"

"Yes."

"I used," she went on, "to think that a man's hand told his history: his history in love, especially. With some men, to touch them was to feel their skin running backward, away from one's fingers. Jerry's hands were rough. I'd hold one–like this–and with my eyes closed it was like touching the scales of a fish. I've known men whose hands had a way of curving, of cupping, even when their thoughts were miles away from a woman. Jerry's did. When we were first married I used to die with embarrassment, thinking the other women saw in them at those moments what I did. In our early days together, to see those hands lying idle on a chair arm or on the dinner cloth would make me almost swoon with longing and impatience. A smooth, smooth skin," she observed. As she drew away, her nails once again scratched across his palm, and through the hairs that grew densely up to and even between his knuckles.

"Not a farmer's hand," he said.

"Don't move. Sit here beside me, on the floor. Take some of my blanket to keep the draft off. We have a few more things to say, and I would like to touch your face, if you will let me."

He got down, a little stiffly, but his constraint had passed off, and he wished that she would ask to touch his hand again in a moment, for the warmth was coming back into it.

"Here we are," she said, "two elderly people who have reached –in my case, almost gone beyond–the time of life when we might have known friendship. Yet, we will not be friends. I think we will not?" she added.

"No, not friends," he agreed.

"Perhaps cordial enemies?"

"I do not believe that you care for cordiality."

"I may not," she admitted. "All my life I have either loved or hated, and it is hard on me now to have to be tolerant: and one must, I suppose, to be cordial. Yet, it was not always arrogance that drove me to extremes. It was at least partly the belief that toleration is a mean thing, implying a lesser respect for others than the extremes of violence do. Even destruction would be better than our inanition. Look at *me!*" She held up her crooked, crippled hands. They dropped again. She said, "I believed once that men were born for great ends."

"I think they are, some of them: but I can not believe that the right end will ever justify such an expenditure as you would be willing to make. Your words would fit the mouth of any dictator."

She tapped one hand impatiently on the chair. Her blanket slipped off her knees onto the floor. "You—and the ones like you—have minds that deal in particulars," she said. "I hope for the general end. The greatness that I would wish for is the greatness that is capable of the highest good or the most terrible, rending evil. Between these two lies the nothing of compromise, and the knowledge that threatens to betray my energy every day is that mankind as a whole is incapable of a strong protest or affirmation. Yet, still I hope." She paused. "I have wanted to found my house on a rock," she said. "You will never understand me if you think that my desire to save it is central only to myself."

He saw her right hand grope through the air and grasp the chain of the floor lamp. She pulled it, and now the only light came from the gas fire. Slowly, his irises widened: he could make out the lighter squares of the windows, and through the one in the side wall, beyond Mary Bush's rocker, he saw the stars, brilliant, remote, cold. The shadow of mortality seemed to him then very small, and the shades of heroes and women fairer than the skies flickering and insubstantial. What rock was this? It was the nothing she had earlier proclaimed it to be, and did not partake of the reservation she had just made. It had no more meaning than the ancient children's game of King on the Castle: a jostling, thrusting, noisy game in which someone always got hurt, and no one held the castle for more than an instant. And why struggle if, unlike Lily Loyd, one believed in the kingdom of heaven?

"If you tell me to," he said presently, "I will go."

"This night we have gone too far for that," she replied, and in the darkness he thought he heard her sigh. "Let me touch your face," she said gently.

He turned heavily toward her, tucking the blanket in around him as he settled again.

He lifted his face. "I am here," he told her. Hesitantly, almost shyly, he slipped off his glasses.

Her thick, parchmenty wrists met beneath his chin, and—he thought with pain at the suppleness her gesture required—her hands branched above them and curved around his cheeks. Her nails made a scratchy sound in the stubble of his beard. One hand dropped away, and the fingers of the other touched his thin lips, his nose; her thumb ran lightly across his eyebrows, and with her palm she touched his hair, found out the shape of his head.

"Herbert Komar."

"I am Herbert Komar," he whispered.

The gas flames sputtered behind him; he got to his feet.

For a moment he was dizzy. The room opened out into the luminous dark of the night, and the stars wheeled before his eyes. He leaned heavily forward on the arm of the tapestry chair, and gradually he fell back into the room; and he said, "Lily Loyd!"

He found that he was twisting her hand in his own; and perhaps that cry he had heard in the vaster spaces had been her own cry of pain: but it was not for this that he released her now. He said, softly, "You must be cold," and he knelt again and gathered up the blanket in his arms, and spread it over her, over her hands, her lap; he slipped it in between her legs and the chair.

"I am sorry," she said.

"Why should you be sorry?" he asked, for he believed that love had no room in it for reproaches.

"For what I called you."

"A cipher? It is true," he replied humbly.

"Perhaps. We will see. We will have adjustments to make," she went on.

"Yes: many of them."

"But you are a man," she said. "I had to know."

"And you . . ." he began.

"I am Lily Loyd," she said. "Ah, my friend, do not let me deceive you. Now, in this hour, I tell you that I will try."

"And I will fight."

Though she could not see him, he smiled.

"Then tell her," said Lily Loyd, "that I have said you may have my house. Until you have seen her, she will know nothing of this meeting from me."

"This is our strategy?" he asked.

"A strategy, not a promise. You will understand that. We wait on her word."

"On her word. Then, goodnight. Do you want the light again?"

"I think not."

"Goodnight, Lily Loyd."

"Goodnight, goodnight."

PART SIX

The Extinct Life

· 13 ·

HE WENT home that Monday night in a perilously exalted state: perilous because, had anyone been available, he would have burst out with his news.

And his news? It was so much greater than the sum of its individual parts that he would probably have been able to communicate nothing more than his excitement. Yet, he was disappointed to find the entire household in bed. He knew it was childish, but he wished there were someone to tell it all to. He would have liked at least to have had a friend who lived a distance away: he might have sat down and written him. "I am going to buy a house." That far he got with his imaginary letter while he undressed in front of the radiator. He crossed, in what was now almost an habitual move, to the bureau looking glass. "I am going to buy a house," he assured his reflection. Buying a house was part of it; he wondered though, as he turned away, if it were not the least significant part? "A home," he murmured; "I'm finally going to have a place of my own."

But the statement rang false: he felt his exaltation recede before it.

"Here's a real fight," he said; and how the joy sprang back! "To the death," he added, and he felt his heart begin to pound as it had when he knelt beside Lily Loyd's chair. He strode across the room and flung open his closet door. But no scabbard clattered to the floor at his feet; no armor winked in the light. He caught his pajamas off their hook, and buoyantly thrust the door shut.

"To the death!"

He flourished the blue-striped flanneling, and paused thoughtfully as the legs and arms swished down and struck against his waist. Could one write such a thing, even to a friend? Could one speak so boldly, even in solitude?

"I am trying to buy a house," he amended, "and the old devil who runs it won't let her daughter sell. But," he added, "we'll beat her."

Ah, he thought with a quick surge of an emotion so unfamiliar that he would not give a name to it, the old *devil!*

But I would like, he thought (he picked up his washrag and towel and went out into the dark hall), I would like to say something to somebody. I would like to tell about my night and say that in the very moment of giving up, of telling her I would go, I found myself.

And *she* did it! he thought. She? It did not seem strange to him that this "she" was a being larger and more distinct than Lily Loyd, a she who spilled powder across a dressing table, who trailed after her soft silks, who dropped earrings into the rug. Were her eyes blue? And her temper?

"Uncertain," he said; and splashing water and soap in his face he murmured, "The devil!"

He touched his face with his wet hands, felt the shape of his head.

"Herbert Komar," he whispered.

Behind him, not in the room but pressed, perhaps, against the window pane, were three women, silent, scrutinizing; beckoning him after them into those windy spaces, promising . . . was it revenge they promised?; vowing . . . but he still would not say what it was the women vowed with their glittering, cold eyes. Only, as he fell into bed and felt the darkness steal under his lids, he could not keep it away.

Love, said the dark. "Revenge," he answered; and in his quick sleep he thought a voice replied, telling everything. "Love and revenge," it said, "and death everlasting."

The next morning he was, as he put it, not unaware of its value as satire, himself again. He saw that Lily Loyd's challenge had resulted from her conviction that even if Blanche agreed to the sale, he would not get the house. For if Blanche supported him, the old woman would simply freeze back to her former adamant. And if—if, as Lily Loyd seemed to think more probable—Blanche continued to hesitate, the victory over him would be a swift one. The decision in the old woman's mind lay simply between a quick and a more leisurely gobbling up.

And where was the romance and fire of last night?

He looked through his window at the desolate row of fenced-in backyards that stretched as far as he could see in either direction. There were lights on in some of the houses on the next street, and they wavered in the early morning dark. He had the city dweller's real and persistent horror of the morning, and now it contributed to his soberness. It evoked for him no recollections of brilliant sunrises, no cries of dawn birds in orchards and fields. Who in a city saw the sun rise? The clustered roofs cut off the view. Dawn was, at best, a bloody reflection on the dining room rug; at worst, a yellow light and a heavy mist that gave way so gradually to day that one felt no joy at the renewed triumph of light. One was at work by then, uncovering the typewriter, dusting the desk, pulling out file drawers. A winter dawn in the city evoked for him only the swish of tires on pavements perpetually wet, the distant sound of streetcars dying away on the cold, still air, the pinched faces of men and women crowded together at bus stops. Winter dawn was rain: endless, heavy, cold; it was stillness, the cars, the trucks, and buses scarcely making a ripple on the intense, distressed silence of a city waking. It was fog and electric light and rising to an icy room and going out to a chill garage and a car that would not start.

Today, the rain fell again, heavily and soberly, through the graying darkness. He shivered and put his robe over his shirt and trousers as he went along to the bathroom. This, he thought wearily, was the time for light, and color, and intense heat to stir the dormant blood. This was the time for small, bright rooms, for curtains to hide the dying night and to muffle the slow movements of life along the pavements and streets.

He plugged in the electric heater by the bathtub and stood looking into the round, red core for a moment, glad of the fierce heat on his stiff hands, and the fierce color in his eyes. Inevitably, at these times, his mind went back to that house in Lark Street. Even then, as a schoolboy, he had been obliged to get up in the dark. He remembered how cursorily he had always brushed his fingers across the ice in the water jug and let it go at that. It was too cold to wash his face, to linger even for a moment anywhere but in the kitchen. He remembered his mother's drawn, cross features as she stuffed paper and kindling into the range, and the heavy step of his father on the enclosed stair; and how his mother had looked at him briefly as the steps neared, her eyes eloquent with panic and despair. As the father's mood inclined, so did the day follow: and when the father pushed open the stairway door the boy and the woman held their breath and glanced silently toward him.

He could understand now something of the depression that had so often afflicted his father. It was the depression of rising to a day that was an all too eloquent symbol of his life: a day and a life beginning and ending in darkness: cheerless, cold, shot through with meager rays of light that the gloom quickly extinguished. It was the depression of going on (Blanche Loyd, at luncheon, had revived the old phrase for him), of going on precisely as one was, of knowing all too well the pattern of one's days and life.

The father had often longed for that country he was born in, but he had grown maudlin, and the wife had jeered and said that what he missed was the promise of America in the old country, a promise so dismally withheld from all of them. She called her husband a dreamer, and she called him a failure. Of the last, thought their son, there was no doubt. He had been a man of small learning, inept in his native tongue and worse in English. Because he had been equally inarticulate both in thought and speech, he had expressed his rebellion against his existence through violence: he had struck his wife and children, got into fights at work, at saloons; and consistently lost his job. And got up the next morning, meek, grizzled, pink-cheeked, at the same hour as always, to go out and start again. It was sad that his wife and children had liked him best when he was most defeated; but pity was all they had to offer him, and they gave it generously in his dark hours. At the end of his life they hastened him into the grave in a rush of tenderness.

Pity, Herbert Komar thought, vigorously brushing his teeth, is all failing people can offer or receive. He was grateful to Lily Loyd that she had thought enough of him to extend none of it. She gave instead the points of her sharpest weapons. And he? Had he not offered her a great compliment when he swore to fight her to the death? As he put on his tie and coat he began to recapture some of his former exhilaration. The old devil would lose this round, he determined, whatever might be the final outcome.

His pleasure was cut short.

Mrs. Hlavaty was halfway through her breakfast when he came into the dining room. But she always ate early so she would be free to serve the others.

"Good morning," he said pleasantly, seating himself and taking his napkin out of its ring. "I see I'm the first one.–But not very, is it?" he added, looking at the leaden, dripping day.

"This rain is getting me down," she answered. "I just put the eggs on a couple minutes ago. You'll have to wait a little." She sighed and drank her coffee. "If it hadn't been for that nice weather yesterday, I think I'd have lost my mind."

The opportunity was too good to pass up. "I thought the weather never bothered you?"

"I don't know what would give you an idea like that," she

answered promptly. "If you had my sinuses, you'd notice the weather quick enough."

"I was thinking of what you said Friday," he replied. "You know, the night of your party."

"Yes, and I'm glad you mentioned that, Mr. Komar." She broke off, and stared at the bay window. Suddenly, she nodded her head and held up her hands in a gesture of amazement.

Mr. Komar turned, startled, and saw that their neighbor was standing in the opposite window holding up a large plant covered over with blue flowers.

"She's grown pots of those from a slip of mine," said Mrs. Hlavaty, "and every blessed one of mine died."

Again she nodded, this time more violently, and the lady with the pot kissed the flowers, waved, and turned away.

"She wants to give a couple to the altar guild at her church, but I told her don't be a fool. What does a church want with live flowers? Then she thought she'd take them to some of the old people she calls on, but I said it'd kill them, taking them around that way. African violets are very susceptible."

"I'd say she ought to give you one," Mr. Komar observed slyly.

"I should think so! But will *she?*" she inquired cynically. "I guess not! People are all the same. . . ." She pushed back her chair. "I'll take a look at the eggs."

"I'm in no hurry."

"Well, I am. I want a word with you before the others get here, Mr. Komar."

His heart sank. He had hoped that the violets would divert her. She returned quickly with one little metal cup in which his egg reposed, and pried it out and onto his plate. The egg slid across the cold glaze and settled, quivering, against the farther side of the rim. He put a piece of bread in the toaster and shut the door on it.

Mrs. Hlavaty poured him coffee and settled heavily into her

chair. She pushed a wisp of hair back under her net and dabbed at her nose with the corner of her apron.

"I ran short," she said. "You'll have to fill up on bread."

"This is fine," he assured her, though she ought to have known that one egg wasn't enough to keep anybody going until noon. And when he broke into it he found that the yolk had cooked hard and rubbery. The egg skated away from his fork, dropping flakes of yolk behind it, and he shuddered.

"Oh, I forgot," said Mrs. Hlavaty, but not very convincingly; "you like them soft. Well," she went on, taking a great breath, "that's what I mean." She paused and looked at him expectantly, as if her point had been made. "You better turn over that toast," she said, when he made no response. As he leaned forward to open the toaster she said, "Anyway, like I say, Mr. Komar, I'm just one woman, and I simply can't do everything."

He flipped over the hot piece of toast and rubbed his scorched fingers on the napkin. "That's quite all right. I don't mind my egg this way once in a while, and I'm sure it must be hard to tell what they're doing until you get them open."

"Yes," she said, "but like I say, it's just too much. You'll be surprised when I tell you that I've thought a good bit about selling this place and getting an apartment somewhere where you get a little decent weather. I have a friend in St. Augustine, and he has often urged me to come down." She contrived a rosy blush. "Some days I think I can't go on any longer. After all, who am I making a home for? You just tell me, Mr. Komar, who am I making a home for?"

"Why," he said, "for all of us, I guess."

"Yes, and what do I get out of it?"

He thought it safest to assume a look of intelligent bafflement.

"There!" she said. "You can't tell me. And you're right. I get nothing, not one thing. I get no consideration, no respect. People treat my house like it was a tourist camp."

"I think you're mistaken there!" he protested. "Look how

pleasantly you keep things. You wouldn't find any tourist camp that had your good taste in its decorations."

"Yes, guests have often spoken to me favorably about my home. But like I say, it isn't a real home to them, and they get married or find some dirty little apartment, and off they go."

"It seems to me, Mrs. Hlavaty, that you've been very lucky with your people. Look how long Miss Kasco's been here. And Myron looks to be staying on. And there's me," he added quickly.

"Yes, and there, Mr. Komar, is where it really hurts. You'll be interested to know that I didn't get to sleep till three this morning. I tossed and turned, and what I feel like now you can imagine. I thought, with Mr. Komar leaving us, what'll I do? It isn't so easy to get respectable guests, Mr. Komar. The way some people—I'll name no names—have treated my furnishings, it's plain they never had a real home of their own. That's why I'll take men every time over women: frittering around and using all the hot water for their personal clothing when I'm in the middle of my dishes, and burning the lights half the night. You've been a comfort to me, I'll say that. Mr. Komar is very considerate and thoughtful, and quiet as a mouse. You can ask anyone here. I've said it to them all, and I wish they were the same. He's just like a bulwark to me, I've said. Days when I didn't know whether I was coming or going he's been there with his little quiet ways. He knows a lady when he meets one, I've said. Very thoughtful and always a gentleman, and prompt. Never any owing me two or three weeks back rent. You can tell about people's breeding, I've said, and it's as plain as the nose on his face that Mr. Komar came from really nice people."

"That's nice of you to say, Mrs. Hlavaty," he answered. "I've always thought of you as a good friend."

"Yes," she said, "and that's the hurt. At first I could not believe it. That's just the way I put it to Mildred Kasco. You can ask her. And he and I just as close as *this*, I said." (She held up two entwined fingers.)

"What was it you found so hard to believe, Mrs. Hlavaty?" he asked, and he abandoned his egg and put down his fork.

He saw that she was thrown out of her careful circumlocutions by his abruptness; he turned away and stirred his coffee and drank it with a calm he did not feel.

"How's that?" she said.

He put his cup carefully back in its saucer. "You've made it clear to me ever since Friday night that my friendship has not been welcome to you. I think you ought to tell me why before we say any more."

"Why, *Mr.* Komar!" she exclaimed. "I certainly never implied anything of the kind, and I'll have to ask you to clarify your meaning."

He put his napkin on the cloth and pushed his chair back. "I mean," he said steadily, "that I resent being treated as an intruder in this house. I resent your suggesting that I'm trying to do you some kind of harm. I have lived here ten years, and until this weekend I would not have believed that you could turn your mind against me without one scrap of proof."

He got up.

"If I am such a disappointment to you," he said, "then I will be happy to find another"—he paused, and he saw agony and curiosity plain in her face—"another room," he said, and turned and left.

"I never meant any such *thing!*" she called after him. "I'm sur*prised* at you! Oh, for *shame!* Shame on you!"

But he continued steadily on his way toward the stairs.

"Don't you want any more *breakfast?*" she called. As he climbed the steps he heard a shriek. "Your toast!" she cried. "It's *burn*ing!"

A few minutes later, while he stood in his bedroom putting on his coat, he heard the rest of the household go one by one along the upstairs hall and down the steps, and when he opened his door Mrs. Hlavaty's voice, low and swift, came up the well. She sounded indignant and injured.

As he reached the first-floor hall and opened the vestibule door (it seemed prudent to avoid passing through the dining room and kitchen and going out the back way, as he usually did), the voice ceased. He could imagine the babble that would rise when he was known to be safely out of the house; and, walking around to the garage, he played with the idea of going suddenly in again, as if he had forgotten something. But the trick seemed more on Mrs. Hlavaty's order than on his own; and since she had met such miserable defeat he was willing to allow her the satisfaction of talking about it.

As for himself—he felt marvelous.

· 14 ·

WHEN Mr. Komar called Blanche Loyd at ten that morning a watery sun was already changing the office windows above his desk to bleared, transparent gray, beyond which he could see the mist lifting off the city. By noon the sidewalks were dry, and last patches of snow in alleyways and along curbs were melting. When he picked Blanche up at three o'clock the day was quivering with sunshine, and the air so mild that he thought it safe to open the car windows an inch or two.

She was waiting for him under the marquee at the front of her building, her beige coat unbuttoned and the scarf at her throat lifting and falling a little in the light wind. The sunlight was not gentle with her, he noticed as he leaned across the seat and opened the curb door, or else she was tired. Her lipstick was vivid and harsh, and gave to her mouth the look of transfixion that the doll on her bed wore. He saw as she crossed the pavement that there was a streak of powder across her nose; he saw, too, the fine cross-hatching of lines on either side of her chin, and the colorless down along her cheeks.

"Are you cold?" he asked, when she had got into the car.

"A little. It's not as warm as it looks."

"You look as if the party had been too much for you," he remarked, hoping he sounded casual enough. He let in the clutch and pulled into traffic.

Her eyes were sharp on his face, but not, he thought, curious. "I should have known they'd have you over as soon as I was out of the house," she said. "They were in such a hurry to get rid of me."

He answered, with his eyes on the truck in front of him, "You ought to know your mother's ways by now."

She was silent. Then, "It doesn't matter," she said. "She'd have got to you one way or another."

He laughed. He felt that for once he had the best weapons and the completest strategy. "What a way to put it! I'd have thought that the last thing she'd ever have wanted was to 'get' to me."

"She's pushing you," Blanche answered. "Look out! Look out for that man!"

Twice startled, he swung awkwardly to the right, barely missing the pedestrian who stood in the middle of the street. He flushed as the man called something after them, but he was grateful, too, for the interruption.

"I'd better not talk until we get out of this," he said. "I'm not used to company in a car."

He turned into a narrow street, and they entered the Public Square and drove west toward the bridge over the industrial valley.

He said, "Anyway, I'm glad you could take the afternoon off. I thought we might go for a drive, since the weather's come out, and have dinner somewhere in the country."

"That will be nice. I haven't had dinner out for months."

"One of the people at work is building a place near Yellow Center, right along the highway. We might head there and take a look at it."

They halted, a few blocks short of the bridge, for one of the interminable traffic lights.

"That loft is still for rent!" Blanche said.

"Yes." He looked, as he had done a few nights earlier, at the bold sign. "That's a lot of space these days." The light changed. "Three thousand feet," he read aloud, and then, rashly, "I might take that and rent it out to students."

"You might better," she answered.

They were silent. Presently, he said, "You have great faith in your mother's endurance."

"I have. Look at the valley today!"

The Chevrolet swooped up the incline to the bridge, and he glanced left and then right past the stone balustrades. In the high light the valley appeared shallow and dimensionless; neat: the roads winding serpentine and clearly outlined between fields and factories; the bridges over the river, the buildings, the river itself looking smaller than life-size, and more distinct, as if they were scale models appropriate for an industrial exhibit at an exposition. Ore boats and other freighters—three, four, five of them he counted—were tied along weedy pilings. Beyond them the river mouthed into the lake, superintended by the white and stern brilliance of the Coast Guard station. The lake was gray with ice and snow along the shore, and as far as the rough wall of the breakwater it was placid; but beyond that rocky wall was mutinous, plunging blue. To the west the distant promontories, crowned and crowded with their expensive hotels and apartments and colored signs, broke the swelling water.

The day was now so clear that even the promontory at the mouth of the yacht club lagoon, five or six miles away, was distinct. A silence, but more living than that silence of dawn, brooded over the water and the cliffs and the clustered buildings. The Chevrolet hummed along smoothly, and they too seemed part of the vast clarity and brilliance.

It was a day, he thought, for decisions to be made in, and understandings reached.

"I'd like to have seen all this back a way," he said, "before they filled up the valley and the city spread so far."

"There's a description of it in a novel of Gissing's—do you know it?—the only one anybody ever reads. I can't think of the title. The hero—or perhaps he isn't—walks to the edge of the city when his train pauses here going farther west. The desolation! The lake often froze over in those days, I'm told. People knew when it was solid because wolf packs came across from Canada."

"Wolves," he repeated, and he looked toward the shimmer of Erie and tried to imagine it frozen and motionless, dotted with agile, yelping, snuffling gray shapes. But it was impossible. Today, the city was inaccessible to any manifestation of the natural life. Tornados, blizzards, earthquakes, fires, wolves: they were helpless before the continuity of the city. Only the human element could succumb. Men no doubt would someday succeed in their task of extinguishing human life, but long after they were gone the cities would remain, dotted across the cold globe, monuments to humanity's might and genius, and appropriate epitaphs to humanity's desire to entomb itself at all cost.

"Well," he said, "it couldn't happen today."

They left the business section along the western rim of the valley and entered the wasteland of old streets that had once formed the farthest and finest reaches of the city. They jolted across rough pavements and streetcar tracks embedded in cobbles. These were nighttime sections through which they drove, he thought: by day they ought to have been decently shrouded. These were the streets of midwives and abortions, of petty thieves and day laborers. These were the prey of the dimestore, the big-bargain furniture store, the all-nite restaurant, the funeral home floodlighted like a Hollywood première, and somebody-or-other's ballroom (ladies cordially invited). Here, poverty abandoned its poor attempt at decency and showed itself naked. It was in streets like these that he felt that if man's being rested in God, his salvation was in Fort Knox.

"These sound the knell for Grant," said Blanche. "You want to buy into a cause already lost."

"Grant Street has integrity," he answered. "I can't believe that these streets ever had more than gentility."

"To me, Grant has only its gentility left."

He thought she was wrong, or that, worse, her observation was simply one more small strategy. On his way home a few nights earlier he had driven slowly down the whole length of Grant, examining the declining neighborhood with a passionate sympathy, and preserving in his response only those fine features that had once figured so largely in the street's repute, and which gave even to its decline a grace and dignity: its large trees, the remaining sweeps of lawn, the houses soaring above their dusty, shabby foliage, topped off with cupolas or widow's walks, surrounded by broad porches and attended by ornate, commodious carriage barns.

Blanche looked away from him and out the window. "I remember when west of us there were fields and woods: real woods. We could walk to the lake for a picnic, or take the electric car a little distance and be out in the vineyard country. Now the grapes have almost died out, and the beaches belong to fat women and giggling men, paper boxes and broken bottles."

"People have to have somewhere to go," he pointed out.

"Yes. They have discovered America. One wonders what beaches they sat on thirty years ago, what kind of refuse they trailed after them then? They came upon us with such brashness and good cheer that we scarcely heeded them at first. So much noise and energy: they were bound to settle down, learn to burn their rubbish and take their bottles back to the grocer. Their boldness fooled us, and when we waited they thought us indifferent, and when we saw that what we had thought was innocence was really corruption, it was too late. And perhaps we were not happier or freer in those times when they . . ." She paused.

"When they . . . what?" he asked, and he felt that they were facing at last the large, the vulgar question.

She kneaded her white wool gloves together, and then spread them carefully across her lap.

"I was thinking," she answered, "how much our attitude toward Europe has changed in a century. Not even that long ago Europe represented culture, civilization: all those vague, beautiful ideals that we wanted for our own."

"It still does for many people."

"Does it? I sense a growing general reluctance toward accepting anything Europe still has to offer. Europe is a carcass swarming with disease that kills at the touch. The refugees all come to us, poor souls, death in their faces and in the touch of their defiled hands. No one any more needs to tell us to see America first. We haven't the slightest intention of seeing anything else. And in Europe—are there signs posted there, too, advising the people to see America first? It might seem so, for our cities are full of the exiled, the dying, the hopeless. What have they to offer? They are cut off totally from their dead countries: the vestiges of their cultures and traditions they have left behind, because the ideal of America seen from far off appeared so much firmer and brighter. But they are like animals jumping into the sea to avoid fire, and discovering that they can not swim. They have forgotten or dismissed all that once gave life to the old, and they flounder helplessly, for our new is only an enlargement, an alteration, of what has been before. They see presently that a large ship rides the water, and they paddle, somehow, toward it. The ship hauls aboard these survivors until its sides begin to split with humanity. The food gives out, and untutored, eager people tamper with the engine. Finally, the older passengers take to the lifeboats, and we drift away. We see there was no alternative to our generosity, but we see also that this generosity will finally sink everyone down."

"Would you still run this ship, as you call it, better if there were room for you aboard?" he said.

"How can we know?" she asked sadly. "We have drifted so far that even our signals to it can no longer be seen clearly. Yet, we are not so far away that we can't see the ship veer and plunge in the waves. Occasionally, when the wind is right, a great screaming and babbling is carried over the water; we guess that the present passengers have discovered their common differences and abandoned any thought of unity."

"And who," he asked, "—who was in that original shipload?"

"Men and women who looked back to a shared past," she answered, "who believed in human dignity, and built ample quarters because they did not like crowding. They thought that each man filled a well-defined space of his own, and had the right to consider himself as distinct from his fellows. Each one believed that he was unique and forever important—to himself if to no other. He distrusted the opinions of the many, and did not want either their company or their approval. He doubted that all men were equal even in the eyes of God." She stopped, and then, deciding that having said so much she might as well say the worst, went on. "Even in our tiny boats we are threatened with a loss of freedom, of time to be alone in, for the refugees see us bobbing silently far away from them, and conceiving that we have brought away the maps or the secret of running the engine, they dive into the water and presently come swarming over our sides."

He was shocked at the injustice in her view; he saw that taking to the lifeboats had resulted in a terrible narrowing of the vision of those original passengers and, with the passage of time, surely a misconception even of what the great ship constituted. And to her he was one of those who put up a dripping hand to haul himself into her tight quarters, not content with the concession she had long ago made to him. Yet, he could hardly answer her because, in one major point at least, she was correct: he, like too many of the others, had nothing behind him but the recollection of grave disorder. His parents had explicitly cut themselves off from their heritage in a belief that native wit would make them proper denizens of the new ship. They had failed; he had always known it. He thought of his father's sad, bewildered eyes before the ever-receding dream of America. They had assumed that no more was necessary to run the ship than a familiarity with names and an acquisition of properties similar to those owned by the other passengers. They had no culture, no discrimination, no learning, no dignity, no diffidence. Most terrible of all, they had no awareness even of what they lacked.

But he found this to say. "It is true that we have overrun you, but you never did more for us than let us come aboard. You never wished—as you admit—to share with us. When we approached, you drew away into your tight circles, and naturally, because we knew nothing at all, we believed that you must be saying things that it was vital for us to learn. As, for a while, you were. Now, if we could know the truth, it might be that your reticence is really due to your having forgotten the meaning of your tale. You could, if you spoke at all, only say us words, and we would know as little as before. Perhaps we came upon you too quickly in the beginning, and thinking there was no time for gradual change you clung to what you had and held it even after its life had withered away. But you have never been a sharing people. You are a people harsh, austere, just, and cruel. To you, our hanging together is a sin, and our confusion is a just dispense from a Providence even a little higher than you are. I understand now why your mother denies me her house; she is close enough to the old law to understand how it thought about things; and I understand, too, your hesitance, for you have only the letter, and you cannot fathom its meaning." When she failed to make any reply, he asked, "Are you angry?"

"I haven't as much right to be angry as you have."

"I hadn't meant to say so much."

"Nor I." She laughed. "We've got rid of *our* gentility. Shall we really find there's integrity beneath it?"

"Yes, we've at last done that. As for the other . . ." He looked at her quickly. "Well, is it a fight to the death? That will prove it."

"If it were only to the death!" she said. "I am afraid it's a fight to inconclusion."

"I hope not. This day will settle it."

"Too much light," she said. "It flattens things. It makes the deeps look shallow, and we will go down in innocence."

He sighed. "There's our great difference again."

They had left behind the denser fringes of the city and now passed along streets lined with big houses. Occasionally, at the end of a short side thoroughfare, they could catch a glimpse of the lake. The walks were full of schoolchildren and women pushing baby carriages. Presently they crossed a bridge over another, deeper and wilder, valley. Beyond it lay open country.

"She primed you well," Blanche said.

"If you mean your mother, you're right: but not wholly. My fellows have pushed me off the ship. I find myself neither confident of them nor of you, you see. One of you cries for conformity, and the other for uniqueness, but I notice that it is not only the one side that is quick to drown the heretic." He laughed suddenly, buoyantly. "Well," he said, "I'm a foreigner!" He felt extraordinarily free—not happy, but free. The bold word was out, and at last they might expect to get on to something. He looked at her, and it seemed as if his boldness had transfixed her. She sat absolutely still, scarcely breathing. The sun struck off her glasses so he could not see her eyes, but her lips were pressed tight together. "But why?" he cried. "If I can admit it, surely you must not be afraid? I'm a foreigner. You condemn me for it: why not admit it? What's happened to your famous honesty—and your kindness, too?" But as still she did not answer, he said, "Surely it's late for you to go on being kind by being evasive, and honest by telling me your mother's views and none of your own. Come, I'm a foreigner. What are you?"

"I . . . am not," she said through those stiff, vivid lips.

He felt pleasure and even a perverse happiness in his sudden urge toward cruelty. He was not above, he thought exultantly, taking his revenge. "You can tell me who you're not," he said. "Now tell me who you are."

"I am myself," she answered sullenly.

But she could not push him back. "Your name," he insisted. "Tell me your name." He sensed her struggle, and when she did not give it to him he pressed his advantage. "You aren't Tom Mix?" he suggested. But when she remained silent he felt his strength collapse. He said, bitterly, "Ah! you are so bold!" He asked, "Is this the support you will always give me?"

How large his question was neither of them may have realized at the time, but something of its portentousness sounded between them. They went on a little way in silence.

The road wound across slow risings, bent leisurely around dense stands of oak, and burst out between level brown fields. No cars passed them, and the silence and the space seemed to mock the energy of their human endeavor. Even in anger they had kept their voices low. Now, he slowed the car and pulled off the road.

"I–"

"Blanche–"

"No, go ahead."

"Tell me," he commanded.

"Have I failed you?" she asked piteously.

"Blanche . . ."

"Tell me! *Tell* me!"

"Dear Blanche . . . dear Blanche. Last night I saw your room. The doll, and the bed, and the mirror. The jewel case." He leaned toward her. "I must know," he said, "which you are–the woman of the dead doll or the woman who spills powder across her dressing table and drops an earring in the carpet."

She turned away and rolled her woolen gloves into a tight ball.

"Please, tell me."

She looked into his face, soberly, sadly. "I am Blanche Loyd."

He felt his heart sink. "No," he said, drawing away, "no. It means nothing for you to say that now." He turned the key in the ignition. "I was right," he said slowly, "that day at lunch.

When you said that selling the house would be a surrender to the way things are, you really did mean me. I am the way things are."

He was sick with disappointment. Perhaps, he thought, Lily Loyd was correct: honesty never solved anything. He was overcome by a terrible helplessness such as he had rarely known since those occasions, long ago, when he had watched his father strike his mother in anger and had stood back as she ran sobbing out of the house, not wanting either her husband or her children to witness her humiliation. Then, as now, he had felt he could do nothing, nothing at all to change the way things were.

He shut off the ignition again and twisted himself until he was facing her. "If you would look at me," he said; "if you would try to see me. You want to stand apart. Is it fair, then, to shove me into the crowd? Is it fair?"

"I am looking at you," she answered, so softly that it was a full moment before he understood the cruelty of her reply.

"That leaves us nothing more to say."

"Doesn't it? Doesn't it?" she asked wildly. "No, I can think of more to say than that. Let me tell you what I see in you.—Don't stop me. You ask for boldness. I see a man who is kind and gentle: a quiet man, who never causes fuss or bother. An ideal employee, no doubt in his time a dutiful son. I see a man who has never lacked anything, because he's never wanted anything since he took his box off its runners and packed his childhood away in it. Gentle, loving, dutiful, honest, kind—no, not one in a million. Far from it. One *of* a million. You cover the earth, you and your brothers, waiting to inherit it." She snorted angrily. "You have me so clear in your kind, gentle mind. I'm a doll on a bed or an earring dropped in a rug. Where do you and the others learn this divine simplicity? Is it the Word of the Lamb flowing in your veins? Life is a joke, I tell you, and the joke is that there should be so many created who never understand the funny line. It's a tragedy filled with onlookers who chatter about an accident when the king lies bleeding with his eyes torn out. It's an art gallery full of Red Cross women rolling bandages, and a church crowded with bingo players. The prophetic Christ! Was it a promise or a warning when He said the meek should inherit the earth? You ask why I can't see you alone; you might better ask how I can distinguish you at all—*gentle* man."

He said, "I can't answer you," and to his astonishment she began to laugh. He listened, still incredulous, but there was no doubt that genuine amusement provoked her. She groped in her bag for a handkerchief, and wiped her eyes.

"Of course you can't," she agreed. She took a deep breath. "Well—Herbert. Once again I'm sorry, sorry if I've hurt you, that is."

"That's all right," he answered stiffly. "I told you I wanted us to get the air clear."

She blew her nose, "I doubt we've done that, or ever will." He felt her looking at him with curiosity. "Herbert," she repeated. "Should I feel uneasy calling you that? Do you mind?"

"No."

"I can't get accustomed to the speed with which people lop off surnames, but there comes a time . . . how long have we know each other?"

"A week; a little more than a week."

"Is that long enough, do you think?"

"I imagine the usurpers measure these things differently from the passengers in the boats."

"I was rude—really rude—wasn't I?"

"You've been rude most of the time." He stopped himself. "No, that isn't really true. You have been kind—but the . . . the person who said that yours was a kindness that killed was perfectly right. You've been honest, too—you've just never gone far enough with it."

"And you've been . . . what have you been, Herbert?"

"Patient," he replied.

"Yes, like a cat after a mouse."

"Not at all: like a mouse waiting until the cat will fall asleep."

She brought out a cigarette as she put her handkerchief back in her purse. "Give me a light," she said.

He reached inside his coat for the lighter, and flicked it open. "That's lost its ceremony."

"I began you with small things," she answered, bending to the flame. "I wanted to show you the measure of complication in details. You can't say that now we're onto larger issues you haven't benefited."

"Have we got on to larger issues?"

"Don't you think so?"

"Then why did you laugh just now?"

"Because—" She blew out a cloud of smoke. "Simply because I go on and on making the kind of generalizations I despise. The Herbert Komars of the world seem to me to do great wrong: that is, they do nothing at all. You frighten me, you and the rest, because you don't believe in struggle, ambition, boldness; if you don't hate, you don't love, either. You are the people who represent what politicians love to call the great backbone of the nation, and I suppose they're correct. But the backbone loses its resiliency, its firmness, its very reason for being when the heart stops." She looked at her cigarette distastefully, and crushed it out. "The backbone, so solid and sure of itself, so large in size compared to the poor heart, denies its life. For this I condemn you, but"—her voice softened—"all my accusations are like quicksilver. When I try to put my finger on them and call them Herbert Komar—*this* Herbert Komar—they split and slide away. Then I feel cruel; I condemn you only to make me feel my own thousand ills. I laughed . . . I was laughing at my own pomposity."

It had grown almost dark, and now, when he switched on the headlights, the evening seemed to enclose them in its dying, greenish silence.

"Herbert," she said, so quietly that her voice might have been only the whisper of longing in his own heart, "look at me."

In the last light her lips were startling in their unnatural red. He shivered and looked away. One part of him stood off, even in this terrifying and desired moment, and commented on the fix his wish for a house had brought him to. In his decorous youth and young manhood moments such as this had been rare, for parents had danced alert attendance, parlors were brightly lit, and conveyance was (mercifully?) by streetcar. But decorum had vanished with the age that enclosed his youth, and he had no other experience to prompt him. Nor did books ever give one a step by step account of what one did. Their authors assumed that instinct would bridge the initial distance, forgetting that instinct is as dead as decorum.

He wanted to say, "I do not know what to do," but his pride had withered enough this afternoon, and at its most important point of all he would not willingly suffer a greater diminution.

"I knew a woman once," he said, clearing his throat, "who never had a beau in her life."

"Then you can add to your list one who has had too many."

He smiled. "You are vain."

"Only in retrospect." She waited expectantly for a moment, and then said, "Give me your hand, Herbert."

He pulled off his glove, which promptly fell to the floor, and put his hand on her lap. His arm was so weak that he scarcely had the strength to put it out.

Her own hands, warm and just a little rough, closed round his fingers and palm, much as Lily Loyd's had done the night before.

"What a cold hand!" said Blanche.

Much as Lily Loyd had said.

". . . The feel of a man's hand," she murmured, "and the hair along the back. And a man's square wrist: see, I can box it," and she did, lightly, with her thumb and index finger. "And a man's face," she whispered, and she touched his chin, and brought him gently closer to her. Her fingers brushed his cheeks and his hair, and slowly she lifted off his glasses and put them down on the seat between them.

"They won't be crushed there," she said slyly. She laughed at the quick flush that burned in his cheeks.

"That wasn't very kind, either," he said.

"I don't want to be kind."

"You aren't."

"Then, how will you fight me?"

"I can't," he answered humbly.

"Then give me your allegiance–foreigner." She leaned toward him, and he brought up his arms and shyly, awkwardly, slipped them around her, holding onto her as if she were a sack of straw.

"Be careful of your glasses," she whispered against his ear. "Take off your hat."

"Oh, Blanche," he said, "don't make jokes about me."

He felt her body stiffen, and her hair brushed his cheek as she leaned away from him. "I make jokes because I'm frightened. Oh, hold me a little minute not as if I were the doll on my bed."

He moved toward her, reckless of his glasses, and tightened his grip. But he was afraid to face her, and continued like a pilgrim at sea to peer over her shoulder as if he were looking for land.

"At our age," she said, "we have to learn about love all over again–how beautiful and silly it is, and how dangerous."

"Not dangerous," he answered innocently; "not at our age."

She gave a gasp of laughter, muffled because he had forced her head down against his coat collar. "I didn't mean that," she said.

He lifted her from him and kissed her on the cheek. The noise was startling in the quiet dark.

She wriggled in his arms. "Let me loose. I'm past the age where I can bend like a willow."

He released her so suddenly that she had to grasp the car seat to pull herself erect. They were both breathing heavily, but less from excitement now than from exertion.

"I'm sorry," he said, for even in his pride that dispassionate part of him had surveyed his constraint and ineptitude.

"I'm not," she answered, and he hoped it was kindness that made her misinterpret his remark. "But that was enough."

Now he was certain that she had gone as far as she intended

to, his pride made him bold. He caught her sleeve roughly, and with a good semblance of passion. "Blanche–"

But her dexterity was far greater than his. She picked up his glasses and held them out. "Put these on before they're broken."

He slipped the temples over his ears, and the night sprang into an embarrassing clarity. Without his glasses, he had been enclosed in a soft, fuzzy world, close and intimate, but now the shabby interior of the Chevrolet was restored, and beyond the windshield the pale evening road, the empty fields and naked woods. A car went by them fast, and in the rear view mirror he saw the headlights of another approaching. Their intimacy vanished sometime between the passing of the first and that of the second. Blanche pulled a pocket mirror out of her bag and, peering into it, poked hastily at her hair and resettled her hat. The action, habitual as he knew it probably was under many circumstances, seemed to throw into relief the incongruity that had given rise to it. He sat silent and stiff beside her, overwhelmed with horror at the situation they had gotten themselves into, even while his male pride continued to commend him for an initiative which, as is customary with male pride, it attributed to his own daring.

"I've forgotten," said Blanche, restoring the mirror to her purse, "what it is you say at a moment like this." She snapped the catch and said thoughtfully, "On the other hand, perhaps I never did have a remark for an occasion like this, because there never was one in an automobile before. I suppose this present generation has had to evolve a wholly new kind of dialogue. Love on the front porch was simple: one opened the screen door and went into the house."

"Maybe they don't say anything," he suggested.

She put out her hand and in her turn touched the sleeve of his coat. When she replied, the constraint was gone from her voice. "Maybe they don't. Maybe that's how they know they're in love, when they can stop talking." Her grip tightened. "Maybe that's why I want to talk, because I'm more afraid than ever."

She shivered, and turning away from him began to draw on her gloves. "Start the motor so we can turn on the heater."

A car came along the highway heading toward them, and she added hurriedly, "Let's get out of here. It's the innocent ones like us who always get caught by the police."

"Do you want to have dinner now?" he asked. "Then we can go and take a look at that house I spoke of."

"Yes. Let's do it that way–if you think we'll be able to see the house now."

At the next crossroad they turned south toward Yellow Center. There was a roadhouse on the edge of the town, and they had dinner in what had once been the bay window of someone's living room. There were few other diners, but the service was slow and it was nearly eight before they finished their meal. During the dinner a heavy and not unpleasing lassitude settled on Mr. Komar. The future, dark and unbounded as it might be, lay beyond the ring of light on the tablecloth, beyond the half-circle of windows, somewhere in the winter night. If this was only temporary relief, it was no less satisfying, and he felt an unqualified pleasure that he had given Blanche Loyd at last a table with a cloth, a floor with carpeting, shining silver, and even a spray of red carnations in a cut-glass tumbler.

He told her about his difficulties with Mrs. Hlavaty, and Blanche listened as if she were not personally involved in the controversy. But during dessert she suggested that he look right away for another room, and the implication that a room in some other house was his only alternative dislodged their mutual ease, as if the air reverberated from some faraway explosion. Silently, they slipped back into their roles as antagonists.

Their meal finished, he would have preferred to whisk her back to Grant Street as quickly as possible. But to do so would have been to admit that their constraint had won out even over the bold moment in the car. They were obliged to go and look at the house that the man in his office was building.

"It's late," he said, as they got into the car, "but it won't take long to see it. If we go back by this road we have to pass the site, anyway."

"I don't mind." Blanche yawned. "Thank you for dinner. It's nice for a change not to know what you're going to have. I get so tired of planning menus with one eye on what we have to spend and the other on what Annabelle can cook."

He swung out of the parking lot, past the illuminated sign at the entrance, and she leaned back in the seat and closed her eyes. The night was clear and dry, and the road empty. She made no attempt to talk, and the end-of-dinner friction soon died wonderfully into peace. Mr. Komar speeded up to fifty, and the old car seemed to skim past the barren fields. They had gone perhaps a mile when, up ahead, he saw a huge pile of dirt near the road, and a wooden shack. He began to brake, and Blanche opened her eyes and sat up. As they drew in toward the curb she cleared a circle on the window beside her and looked out.

"Is this the place?" she asked incredulously.

The car stopped.

He understood her surprise. There was not much to be seen besides the raw earth, some piles of lumber, and a low brick foundation.

"That's it," he said, more enthusiastically than he felt, for the evening threatened once again to collapse, now that its focus was revealed as no more than this hole in the ground. "The basement's in."

"I see. Well. Shall we get out and look at the hole?"

"Do you mind?"

"Not if it isn't too muddy."

She opened the door, and he slid across the seat after her. It had grown much colder, and the bitter starlight made the night seem colder still. They stood at the curb. A board walk led up over the property to where the low brick topping to the foundation rose above the level of the ground. He took her arm and they walked slowly forward, their steps making a solemn rattle on the planking.

"Well," she said again. She looked around the empty landscape. The highway was unlighted, and only an occasional automobile flashed by. The lights of Yellow Center were invisible, but far away down the road the roadhouse sign blinked red and yellow. "He'll have privacy."

"It'll be a good-sized place," said Mr. Komar, looking at the foundation.

"I wish we would see it more clearly."

"I'll turn on my spotlight."

He hurried back to the road and started the engine, and pulled the car into the rough driveway at one side of the property. The spotlight threw the front wall into brilliant relief, and against it Blanche Loyd looked for a moment enormous and alien, both to the countryside and to himself. But as he returned to her she smiled and moved to his side.

"I can't see much more than I could before," she said, "but I'm glad of the light."

She drew her coat closely around her. He took her arm. They stood, backs to the spotlight, looking down into the blackness.

"Will someone, someday, fight for this house?" she murmured.

He swung her toward him. "Blanche," he said, "I haven't told you what I brought you out for today."

He felt her body slump, and she half-turned her head away from him, so that against the light he saw her ragged profile.

"I don't want to start it again," she said. "Not now. Tell me later, Herbert. Tell me when I can't see you."

"Blanche, I saw your house last night: all of it."

"I know. You told me you'd seen my room. Do you think I'm such a fool that I can't guess what she got you there for?"

"Do you know why she did it?"

"Yes." She pulled away from his grasp and walked to the edge of the ditch around the outside of the foundation.

"Be careful!" he said sharply. In the distorting light she seemed to sway toward the edge.

"Don't tell me about it," she repeated dully. "I don't want to know what she told you."

He answered bitterly. "She knew her mind, at least."

"She's closer to the old law. Isn't that what you told me?"

He went over to her and caught her around to him, and holding tightly to her arms he said, "She knew you were a coward."

She opened her mouth as if to protest, and blindly, desperately, he began to shake her.

"Well?" he demanded.

"What? What do you want?"

"Give the house to me. Give me the house. Give it to me!"

"I can't think. Let me go!"

"Are you going to fail me—and yourself?"

"I don't know." She began silently to cry.

He slipped his arms closer around her; her head dropped on his shoulder. "Blanche, Blanche!" he said. "It isn't the house. Will you go on being a prisoner forever?"

"Oh, God!" she moaned. "Why can't you let us alone? Why don't you go away? I never wanted to sell the house. It was talk, talk—I wanted to get even with her. How could I know that fool would take me seriously and send you to me?"

"I'll never let you alone now," he said. "I'll never go away."

She struggled in his arms, but he held on to her grimly, and they swayed at the edge of the ditch. The spotlight played full on them, and a sudden sense of conspicuousness made him release her.

But he was not in time.

A car going west toward Yellow Center slowed; he heard a raucous laugh. Then, above the noise of her oblivious weeping, a cruel, amorous whistle rose and slowly died into the night as the car gathered speed and roared away.

· 15 ·

"SHE's sick."

He was glad that the porch in Grant Street was unlighted; he could feel the fear swarming into his eyes as he looked at the grim features of the housekeeper. He stepped farther away from the haze of light that filtered around her thick shoulders and out into the night. The pair of white wool gloves he continued to hold outstretched, a talisman that was threatening to fail of its function.

"She left these in the car last night," he said quickly. "I thought she might be wondering where they were."

"I'll give them to her."

Mrs. Mentone extended her arm around the narrowly opened storm door.

"I thought that–"

"I'm sorry. She can't see you. She can't see anyone. She came home from the office late this morning, and she's been in bed ever since."

"Sick," he repeated; but he held the gloves just beyond her impatient reach. "But, last night–"

"Last night! Coming in white as the dead. Coming up the walk *alone*. It's enough to scare anyone, climbing up between those bushes at the steps. I thought we'd let you understand what this neighborhood was like?"

"She got out before I could–"

"I saw it all. I saw her slip on the walk, and you sitting there in the car."

"Sick. A cold?" he asked with desperate urgency.

"Fever and chills. I thought she was out of her head, rushing past me with her hat and coat still on, and when I got around to the living room she'd slid the door shut. I was *wild*—with Lou out somewhere, and the two of them closed up together. I tell you they had it out that time! I'll take those gloves, please. I've got my hands full enough, with her in bed and the other one sitting like cast iron in that chair. What am I supposed to do? Do you know what the old woman said to me just now, before you rang? She said, stop walking around me, I'm not a public monument. And I told her, I'll thank you to remember, Mrs. Loyd, that I'm a lady, and that I expect to be treated like a lady."

"Did Miss Loyd give you any message?"

"And *then* she said . . . A message? No, no message. That was a kind thought, coming all the way out here with her gloves, though she won't need them for a while yet, I'm afraid"—and Mrs. Mentone groped toward them once more.

"Mrs. Mentone—"

"*Mr.* Komar, I can't stand here the rest of my life. *If* you please."

He handed in the gloves, but as she moved to close the storm door he caught its edge and pulled it farther open. For the first time the stillness of the house reached him. Beyond Annabelle Mentone's back he saw the dancer on the newel post frozen in her attitude of freedom. The only light in the hall came from the cluster of bulbs the figure held aloft. The kitchen was dark. He pictured the dark lying matlike across the whole house, muffling the slight human commotion. He saw it bearing up and creeping over the woman in the upstairs room. The doll with the frozen mouth had already vanished down into it; it clung to the flakes of dust on the oval looking glass. He thought of it making a cave inside which the old Lily sat in her tapestry chair in a darkness that was even completer, that no life, no urgency, no conviction could lift away. He said, forcing his eyes to meet Mrs. Mentone's, "If I've done anything wrong—If you'd tell me what it is I've done to them."

"You've done what *she* wanted," answered the woman, nodding toward the closed great door into the living room. "Now you can go away. You can do that *for* them. If you'll only let us alone . . ."

"But that's not fair!" he protested; and then, himself gesturing toward the sliding door, "Can't I talk to *her?*"

"Her? She doesn't see anyone any more. No. No, there's no one here for you to see."

"But Monday night—two nights ago: she saw me then!"

"Well—and you saw her. You did as she told you. What would you have to say to her now?"

His hand dropped from the door. "I don't know."

"Then—goodnight."

He turned away, and crossed the porch. He knew that the woman behind him did not move. He felt her eyes, intent and cold, on his back. As he reached the top of the steps he heard the storm door shut. She was gone? Yes, gone.

But there were footsteps on the boards, and as he started down a hand touched his coat.

"Listen," she said, "it's all over. Whatever it was, it's done. You go away and find yourself something—something with life to it. There's nothing for you here."

"Is she very ill?"

"How can I say?" She shivered and clutched her big arms together against her stomach. "She's so honest. She can't name it, so she says nothing's wrong. But she won't get up."

He remembered that yesterday, in the twilight car, Blanche had spoken of danger. "She was all right!" he said insistently. He was overcome with shame, remembering how he had taunted her, asking if she were Tom Mix. How could he have said a thing like that?—a thing like *that!*

"We had such a nice dinner," he explained.

Mrs. Mentone's voice had softened when she replied. "I do think she has a little cold. There's mud on her shoes. Were you out on the damp ground last night?"

No, no! he wanted to protest. Not we two. There were a man and woman standing there, a pair of idiots; not Blanche, no; not me. We came right back from dinner, a very pleasant meal in a nice roadhouse near Yellow Center. I was proud of those carnations, and we had a cloth on the table.

"Not for long," he said sullenly.

"It doesn't take long at her age. Now, you just forget it. She's a little gloomy with the 'flu, is all. And Lily—well, she's feeling too much life in her bones."

"You don't say anything," he answered bitterly.

"Well, well . . . what should I say? Here's the end of the line. It's been quite pleasant, Mr. Komar. We're going, too, Lou and I, as soon as he finds a job. There's nothing more for anyone here."

Snow began to fall, broad splashes of it that struck the steps, the sidewalk, and melted.

"Oh, dear!" said Mrs. Mentone. "Another bad night. Here we are scarcely done with fall and I feel as if the cold had been with us forever."

He halted with one foot on the first step. "Could we talk somewhere?" he asked. "I wanted to ask you before. And now . . . if I can't get in, could you come out?"

"Oh, I couldn't! I'd never have the chance. Besides, what would there be for me to say?"

"You could tell me—about them. You and your husband can leave, but I haven't any place else to go. If you'd meet me"—he paused—"down the street," he said, "in that drugstore at the corner of Kingery. Just for a little while, a few minutes."

"T*onight?*"

"Yes."

"I wouldn't make any promise. You'd have to wait around on the chance . . . They both watch me. I'll have to say it was you at the door just now, and if I go right out they'd be sure to know. Blanche wanted some cigarettes, though." Her voice dropped, conspiratorial. "Wait an hour. Can you do that? If I haven't come by then, I won't be. And you'd better hope I won't, and go on home and leave them as they are."

"I'll wait," he replied as she withdrew and hurried, huddled over, into the house.

He went down the steps and along the slick-shining walk to his car. He got in on the curb side, and the motion of sliding across the seat reminded him of twenty-four hours earlier, when he had slid out after Blanche Loyd to look at that other house which was only a foundation.

He sat in the cold car for a few minutes, jingling the keys against the steering wheel, remembering the first time he had parked in Grant Street. Where across the long days that intervened had he dropped the vision of lighted porches, of parties, and ladies in rabbit-fur coats? How he loved now that comfortable, unquestioning, shy man who had halted his automobile and pulled out his watch: too early (ah! years and years too late!), and hesitated, waited a little. Like a mouse for the cat to fall asleep. Oh, no! he protested. That was a *nice* man who sat there, a man getting on in years, with some money put aside (dollars to a teller: but that was nothing to sneer about; that former life had been spacious, tranquil). What a pity!–and did dreams, all of them, always end this way, in confusion and shame? If they did, then that placid man whose life was as spacious as a rented room, that placid man had known that there was no use from the beginning. What had precipitated him out upon the glittering floor? Too many tuna-fish salad sandwiches, too much gardenia toilet water, a quiver of mirth on the face in the bathroom glass? *Mr. Komar's very settled in his ways.* Oh, and I *was!* he cried; I was!

He started the engine, and the heater set up its whirr and click. It reminded him sharply of last night, the only sound in the car as they drove along the winter roads to the city. Blanche had sat so quietly that he had turned to her as they got back into the lighted boulevards, wondering . . . But what had he been afraid of? That she was going to faint? He could not say, even now. Her fainting would have been the last bitter absurdity. But he had been silent, too, writhing under the humiliation of that amatory whistle. He had known no words that would ease them out of their cruel self-consciousness. One could face the stern, the tragic. But farce, like happiness—like that brief happiness they had glimpsed earlier in the day—farce and happiness could not be met by accustomed responses. It was cruel that they had talked when they should have been silent, and been struck dumb when silence destroyed the whole timid web of mutuality.

He did not know where to go. The twenty or thirty minutes that must certainly pass before Mrs. Mentone could dare to think of leaving sagged against his appalled heart. But he had nowhere to go any more, not even a room. "Even," he thought, wryly. Mrs. Hlavaty's new, determined geniality, the perfect eggs at breakfast this morning, the book Miss Kasco had left on his bed, which he had found when he went back last night, were all part of the ferocious comedy.

He pulled into the line of traffic and drove slowly along the length of Grant Street. The snow began to fall faster, and the flakes, diminished in size, bounced on the hood and fenders and swarmed against the headlights. Five blocks beyond the Loyds' house the street abruptly degenerated. Here was the oldest part of Grant, he had been told, built in the seventies and intended to be one of the fine avenues in the young city. Only a few great stone houses remained to mourn for the grand intention, and these had been indefatigably divided and subdivided. Every window showed a light: a floor lamp in this one, an electric bulb dangling from a cord in another: the desolating urban quality—discrete points of light that somehow denied contiguity. Sometimes stores—for furniture, dry cleaning, groceries, wine—had been built on the fronts. In other blocks the houses had been pulled down—a hospital occupied the site of what had been, perhaps, a whole row; a Y.M.C.A. stood in what must have been the yard of the tall house squeezed against one of its blind side walls. Only the hospital and the association for Christian young men stood firm: the shops and lodgings had a temporary identity akin to their rapidly shifting occupants. He knew that Blanche Loyd was correct: Grant Street was a lost cause.

The cold humour of indignity pervaded him. It was immoral that a street should so far decline, that the iron stag or the frilly summer house—it didn't matter which—should be hauled away, so that a later generation with another, grander intention could erupt brick foundations and plaster walls on their sites, and put electric signs outside these walls, and bar stools or steam pressers within; that progress should be always a decline, that age should foster not wisdom but concrete and rats, that a street should get itself into a *fix* like this!

"It's not fair!" he said out loud.

It was terrible. To be trapped. To have nowhere to go except blindly forward. He and the street together. And what happened? What on earth really started it all? I should never have gone, he thought; I should have stayed as I was. I'm too old for all this. . . . But one was not a street at the calling of time and men; one was not a house to be sold or mortgaged, haggled over, split up, torn down. There was oneself, whole, unique, to be preserved in dignity, and at any cost, at any cost. "And I will not," he said despairingly, turning the car in a wide circle and starting back, "I *will not* end it like this."

No, not in farce, not with the recollection of the spotlight playing in his eyes and that strident whistle calling the whole world to witness. It did not matter that to the speeding youngster he was an anonymous figure, forgotten . . . how soon? His pride had shriveled in that public glare. Now, tenderly, with a fierce protectiveness, he nursed his own self-love. He had deteriorated without grace, been renovated without compassion: the iron stag vitalized with colored lights that made it ridiculous and oh! how touching!

Tonight, what he was doing was only another submission to the way things were carrying him. A clandestine meeting with somebody's betrayed wife, behind them the bulk of a great house hidden in a winter storm! And he? A betrayed lover. Yes, a lover betrayed of himself. How much more desperate was his plight than that of Mrs. Mentone with her paltry Lou. He could not bear the indignity of his role. If the stag had only known, at the dark hour, what its true nature was! But how could it have?—standing quiet and still on its green lawn.

"Poor *thing!*" he cried to the night and the storm, and he slowed down and drew into the curb near the drugstore. He sat shivering in the dark, for the temperature in the car dropped quickly after he cut off the motor, and the minutes, too, dropped one by one.

I'll have a hot bath, he thought, and then I'll just curl up. I'll get a *Post* while I'm in the drugstore. And tomorrow . . . He pulled up his collar and thought of sinking into bed. It would be a good night for the extra blanket, the pink one in the bottom drawer whose color gave the room so much warmth, such a rosy, settled look. There might be some coffee left in the kitchen, and he could take a cup up to bed. And clean pajamas, he decided. There were only the next minutes to get over: she probably wouldn't come. Even if she did, a cup of coffee in the drugstore couldn't take long, and then he could go home, satisfied that she was right and there was nothing for him to do, and tomorrow . . . He honestly couldn't think that far ahead. He imagined rather falling asleep to the hard, steady, insulating rustle of snow. He would close his eyes and curl up his body under the rosy blanket, himself fresh in clean pajamas and just, for a matter of moments, a little more alert than usual with the bitter hot coffee in him, and imagine the snow extending on and on beneath the furious sky; he would sink down in the nothing-to-do-until-morning, and morning away ten empty thoughtless hours beyond the whirling night.

· 16 ·

He woke with a start from his cold half-sleep. From high in the snow-filled air the silence-inflated chimes of the church clock ballooned down, settling gently, one by one, on the roof of the car. Nine of them? Yes, nine, he saw, drawing out his watch and holding it close to the lighted dashboard. She would surely have come by now; or had he missed her? She would know his car; she would be watching for it. Well, thank God, she wasn't coming; he'd done what he could. But give her five, give her ten minutes more: give himself ten minutes, that was to say, and conscience would be clear. He twisted in his seat and looked back along the sidewalk in the direction she would approach from. There were no passersby, and when he had turned around once more he saw that there was very little traffic in the streets. The stoplight at the intersection of Grant and Kingery changed to red, to green, to yellow, and only an occasional solitary car halted or moved forward. It was a wicked night.

He shivered and stretched his cramped legs sideways. He smoothed the Indian blanket across the upholstery, and then turned the ignition key and started the engine. As it caught, he saw a face float across the dirty glass in the curbside door. The vague face was succeeded by a gloved hand that rapped softly but imperatively.

With a sinking heart he leaned across the seat and unlocked the door.

"Good work!" said Mrs. Mentone in a penetrating whisper. She hitched up her coat, slid in beside him, and shut the door. "Turn up Kingery to the first stoplight after this one, and then turn right." She relaxed heavily and began to mop her wet face with the end of her muffler. "I don't think they guessed. I didn't leave until the last possible moment. Good thing you waited: I cut it pretty close, didn't I?"

He said in a voice louder than usual, to compensate for her stentorian whisper, "But I thought the drugstore . . ."

"The drugstore? Then what did you start the motor for when I came up? No, no, I thought it over too. There'd be no chance of talking in that place. There aren't any tables or booths, and the counter's very small. And always"–she cleared a circle on the window beside her and looked cautiously out–"always the chance of someone coming in who might wonder what we were doing. Oh, my!" She drew a handkerchief from her coat pocket and blew her nose. "I must look a sight. I nearly froze getting down here." She reached her left hand toward him and succeeded in patting his arm, though she kept her face buried in the handkerchief. "What a night you drew me out on!"

"I had no idea it would get as bad as this. I could just as well have picked you up at the house."

The handkerchief plummeted to her lap. "And what do you think Lou would have said to that?"

"Lou?"

"Say what you will about him, Lou's got a wild temper. What would he think if he saw a car stop outside the house and me get into it with a man?"

"Didn't you tell him I'd asked you to meet me?"

"Lou? With his big mouth? He'd have run right down to the old girl, and *then* I'd have been in for it. No, I told him one of my colleagues that I used to open the second half with blew in town for the evening, and asked me to have a cup of coffee with her."

"I understood Miss Loyd wanted some cigarettes?"

"She found a pack in her desk, so I told her I just had to get out of the house for a while to clear my head. Mother went to bed, luckily, so Lou can keep an eye on her."

"Won't they compare stories?"

"Blanche took a pill. She was nearly asleep when I left." It was plain that she was delighted by her dual strategy.

"In the morning?" he persisted.

"They'll never think of it again."

"And if they should?"

"Mr. *Komar!* I did the best I *could!* Lou knows how bad my veins are. He'd think I was out of my head if I suddenly decided on a walk a night like this." She chuckled, and after a moment added confidentially, "When he gets to thinking about it, he'll remember I never opened the second half with a *woman,* but he won't be sure enough to kick up a stew."

"Miss Loyd might suspect this urge for a walk, too, you know."

"Not Blanche. She's too wrapped up in herself right now to wonder about anything. Besides, she doesn't know how bad it is tonight. She's had the shades down since afternoon."

"Well . . ." he conceded gloomily. "I certainly hope—"

"There, the light's green for us. Make it quick." She leaned forward eagerly as the car drew away from the curb and swung left. "Don't you hate to get caught by a red light?" The implication obliged her to laugh richly. "I mean, I don't drive, but whenever our friends take us for a ride I'm always pushing on the floorboards to get us through lights."

"Straight ahead?" he asked. He glanced back wistfully, but the lights of the drugstore had already vanished into the storm.

"That's right." She straightened her hat and restored her muffler inside the coat. "I'm a nervous wreck. Do you have a cigarette? Oh, wait; here's one in my purse. And I turned the house upside down this afternoon looking for one! Blanche is so huffy about lending hers. So," she went on, as if ending an extensive parenthesis, "I thought coffee so late at night might keep me awake for hours, and after what happened last night I simply have got to get some rest."

He took one hand off the wheel long enough to give her his lighter.

"Well!" she said briskly. "There's a gentleman. The hallmark of breeding every time. If I ask Lou for a light he hands me his cigarette! But he was used to servants when he was young. They had a lot of money, you know, the Mentones. A very big family in the city, and I may say that the way they treated me for a while you'd have thought I was a foreigner, or worse. I could have had plenty better than him, I told them, and with *jobs*, too. Not that I'd really have taken anybody else, though I didn't tell them that. When Lou came into the bar that night—I was sitting having a beer with a girl friend of mine that I worked with—and keeled over sick as a dog, I said you come on down the street to my place and I'll give you a dose that'll either fix you up or knock you clear into next Sunday. So he did, and"—she broke off and gestured wildly to the right. "There's the turn. Oh! We missed the green. If you'd just speeded up a little, you could have gone right through on the yellow. That's in the law, you know. If you'd been hit, you could have sued. Oh, well." She looked up and down the empty thoroughfare. "We could almost go through anyway; there's not a soul around. And," she resumed, "the next day he sent me flowers—yellow roses! He said ours was a romance of July and November. I thought that was beautiful, and so much more honest than the old May and December business. I didn't like to tell him that it was November for both of us, and I was a bit farther on in the month even than he was. I was slimmer then, of course, quite a bit. It's funny, I've put it on and Lou's dropped it off. And he didn't know about my hair during our courtship. But after we were married he had to know that I touched it up now and then, when there was nothing to use except the sink." She sighed. "I wouldn't change it, though. When I think of that room of mine! And cooking over a hot plate, and nothing but damn' women friends. . . . No, November's the real time for mating. When you're young you've got plenty of heat in yourself. November knows the rush of things, and how the year runs out. At night, when I put my feet against his back—I have very poor circulation—I know that I don't care two hoots for those Elks;—

I don't care how bright their eyes are. It's nighttime that counts, more than ever it does when you're young. *She* understands that—Lily, I mean. That's why we get along. But Blanche . . . I don't know. I tell you this," she explained, "because—well, just because I didn't want you to get the wrong idea about what I said the other evening. I wouldn't trade places with either of them. Oh, sure, I envy them having a real home, and some money, but who wants the grave just because it means security? Look there! That's the place. As I was saying—wasn't I?—coffee just keeps me on edge for hours, and I thought—unless you have some principles against it—that we might use something a little more warming. To ward off a chill, you know: I felt a chill coming on when I stepped out the front door." She sneezed. "There!" she cried. And then, "Oh, good! You're sure you don't mind? Here's a spot. Can you fit into it? Aren't you clever! Lou handles a car beautifully, too. Such a little space, isn't it?—and you did it all in one move." She buttoned up her coat. "I've never been in this restaurant before. 'Chez-When,'—what a fancy name! I suppose it's French. It got quite a writeup in the paper when it opened last month. You have to be so careful where you go in a neighborhood like this. The hunkies have moved in everywhere. There's hardly a night I don't read about a brawl or a shooting."

He got out of the car and walked around the front, noting with relief that Mrs. Mentone was correct in considering Chez-When as something more than just a bar. It occupied what must formerly have been two small stores. Over the left-hand door was a sign that said "Grill"; over the door on the right a sign in another color said "Bar." He thought that Mrs. Mentone's eyes followed him a little anxiously through the windshield (she made no move to get out), and his suspicion was confirmed when he opened her door.

"Thank you," she said, popping briskly out. She looked, in the lights of the restaurant, rosy with pleasure at his small attention. "Thank you very much. Oh, my!" She blinked snow off her eyelashes. "My hair will be in strings! It's almost a blizzard, isn't it?"

She put her arm through his and they moved sedately but firmly toward the door marked "Bar." There was a rubber mat laid over the carpet immediately inside, and here Mrs. Mentone paused, clinging heavily to his arm, and stamped snow off her galoshes.

"I know!" she exclaimed. "I'll take them off. That lovely rug . . ."

The lovely rug, he thought, would not have showed the passing of an elephant across it. Its background was a brilliant, aggressive red, its pattern a series of whorls, right angles, and blocks in yellow and light blue. They stood on the mat at the edge of this dazzling growth like hunters hesitating before a plunge into the jungle. Mrs. Mentone leaned her full and considerable weight against him, kicked one foot out backward, and began to pull on the galosh that covered it. She lost her balance, screamed, and hopped along after him as her weight bore them sideways against the wall. Here she managed to pull herself erect, and to put a stockinged foot on the floor. She peered into the galosh that she clutched, and after some struggle extracted from it a red suede shoe.

"Well!" she said breathlessly. "That was almost a tumble. You're strong, aren't you?" She looked around hopefully. "Did anyone see us?"

Mr. Komar now looked above carpet-level for the first time also. His hope was realized, for there appeared to be no one in the room except the barman, who was mopping the floor behind his counter, and did not seem to have observed their agile entrance.

"I'll run into the girls' room a minute," said Mrs. Mentone. She waved her galosh at him. "I'll bet you're wishing you'd never taken me out!" She limped away, still carrying her galosh and shoe. "Order me whatever looks good," she said. "Brandy and coffee would be nice, wouldn't it? Or Scotch?" she flung at him, and disappeared through a door marked with a neat electric sign of a lady with a handglass.

Mr. Komar hung up his coat and went uncertainly along the front of the room to a table just outside the women's washroom. Another couple pushed through the street door and made their way noisily to seats at the bar. Watching their assurance, he felt his own self-consciousness in a public place, and smiled without appreciation at his choice of what was beyond doubt the worst-placed table in the room. Presently the barman came up, having finished serving the others, and Mr. Komar ordered two Scotches with soda. He lacked the courage to ask for coffee for himself.

The man went away, and a moment later the door to the Ladies' Room opened and Mrs. Mentone appeared, splendid and abundant in a knitted dress of a deep coral color. On her left shoulder she wore a bunch of cloth violets. A gold peacock with a tail and crown of tiny green and red and white stones bumped uneasily against her breast when she moved. The belt at her waist was gold also, with a rhinestone buckle, and on her right arm she wore a hinged series of thin gold bracelets. On her left wrist was a silver watch with a black strap.

Mr. Komar sat frozen in his chair, and something far worse than his worst fears began to stir.

"Oh, this is dandy," she said, sitting down opposite him. "Right beside a window, too. I wish it was low enough to see out of." She appeared to recollect herself. She swiveled her eyes toward the couple at the bar, and then leaned far over the table (the peacock lost its precarious footing and jiggled frantically in space). "But," she said in her clear whisper, "do you think it was *wise*—"

"I ordered Scotch," he said hastily. "I hope that's all right."

"That's marvelous." She righted herself slowly. "And perhaps it's just as well not to be too—you know: not to go into hiding. This way, if anybody sees us, they'll know we're not . . . *you* know."

"I thought you said no one would ever find us here," he said waspishly. He instantly regretted his tone, for Mrs. Mentone giggled. "I'm concerned for your sake," he went on.

Mrs. Mentone rolled her large eyes. He would not have believed it possible, but there was no doubt that her eyes revolved in what was patently intended to be a look of delighted female anguish. "Now, if that doesn't sound like the old days! Don't worry. Lou would never think of looking for us here."

"I wasn't thinking of your husband," he replied stiffly.

"Oh. *Her?* She'll never hear about it. *Her* friends wouldn't know a glass of Scotch if it got up and played the bagpipes."

The barman returned with a little tray.

"Mix?" he asked Mrs. Mentone.

"I have quite a cold. I think I'll take it straight down. But if you have a little beer, instead of this soda? . . ."

"Mix?" he asked Mr. Komar.

"Thank you," Mr. Komar answered. "I can do it myself."

As the man went back for her beer, Mrs. Mentone burst into appreciative laughter. "You're a *wit!*" she finally brought out.

"I beg pardon?"

"Ah, now! And you keep a perfectly straight face about it. *That* I *can*not do. I love a joke, but I simply can't keep a poker face. Well . . ." She held up her shot glass. "Here's to . . . here's to life!"

"To life," he echoed, and his glass touched hers.

He drank up quickly.

"Have another," urged Mrs. Mentone when the man brought her beer. "I like to linger, but I know Lou always has three to my every one." She broke off to watch a group of five or six people who came through the door, laughing and brushing snow off their coats. "*She's* pretty," she said, nodding at a redheaded woman who took off her coat to reveal a brilliantly green dress. "It takes a wonderful complexion to get away with a shade like that. I used to be able to, but when the color of your hair isn't . . . isn't *stable* any more you have to be awfully careful what you put on with it." She looked at him almost shyly, and after the waiter had returned and put down Mr. Komar's second Scotch and soda she said, "You haven't told me what you think of my dress."

"I noticed you'd changed," he said.

"I should hope so! You didn't think I'd come to a place like this in a housedress?" She took another sip from her glass. "This is warming, isn't it? I feel quite gay. And, my God, I'm glad to get out of that house for a while! Day and night . . . and the old woman's cane thumping the floor all the time. I hear it in my sleep." Her expression grew abruptly more serious. "And speaking of hearing things," she went on, "I knew something was wrong last night, long before Blanche came tearing in. . . . It came again."

"What came?" he asked.

"The ball. Dragging itself down the stairs. I was terrified, and the old woman'd been so queer all evening. Tense. Once she fell asleep and had a dream, and began to go 'Hoo, hoo, hoo!'—you know, the way old people do when they're upset about something. I woke her up, and she didn't say a word. She just grunted once and then sat in that chair with her eyes shut, pulling away at the doily like she does—I thought it would drive me crazy. Lou was away, and I was furious with Blanche. She knew he wouldn't be home. I don't blame you—how would you have known? But I swear that's the last time they leave me alone that way. It was about nine o'clock that the door at the top of the back stairs opened. I could hear it breathing—I really *could*—and waiting there. Finally, it started down, and just as it bumped onto the first step Mrs. Loyd opened her eyes and looked right at me and said, 'What's that?' Well, between the two of them, I thought, This is it, Annabelle. She dropped off to sleep again, and I sat there, shaking all over. But it didn't come. Things weren't right for it. I don't know. Yes, I'd like another, please. No more for you, Mr. Komar? I hate to be a solitary drinker. Oh, I see, you've got a little left. Now, wait for me. Oh, waiter!" she called after the man. "Water for me this time, I think."

"But nothing happened?" he asked.

"No, that was all, but I knew it meant something."

He began to feel very wise; a pool of sadness, delicious and dark, brimmed quietly in him. "It meant nothing," he said slowly. He lifted his glass.

"I see what you mean. The spectre in the house is Nothing. Oh, shame on you! You've drunk it all up. Waiter! Make that two of them, please."

"Nothing," he agreed; "the spectre is Nothing."

"Nothing is the spectre," said Mrs. Mentone, with a little giggle. "You've hit on something there."

They began to laugh. It was extraordinary, he reflected, how the laughter made him feel even sadder.

"But it isn't funny," he said, struggling with his mirth.

"I know," agreed Mrs. Mentone, making an attempt to straighten her face. "It's tragic. A real tragedy in our time."

They regarded each other solemnly, but it was too much, and they hastily averted their eyes, their bodies shaking with laughter.

"Well, it *is!*" he choked, after an agonizing minute in which the flimsy table between them vibrated with their hilarity.

"I *know!* Those two old women in that old house!" She flung herself back in her chair, and the tears rolled down her face. "Listen, if I laugh much more I'll wet my pants."

"Two old women with a red *ball,*" he said.

"Cut it out! I've got a pain in my side, and—Oh, my God! Excuse me!" She got awkwardly out of her chair and sidled into the Ladies' Room again. At the door she paused, her face rosy and wet, and waggled an admonitory finger at him. Then, in a fresh and disastrous burst of laughter, she disappeared.

He was abruptly sober. He looked around, wondering if they had drawn much attention to themselves. The room had continued to fill up, however, and conversation and the thundering of a juke box had drowned whatever noise they had made. The waiter brought a basket of popcorn, looked at their glasses, and went away.

Mrs. Mentone returned, looking powdered and otherwise restored, and sank into her chair. "Whew!" she said. "I haven't had a laugh like that in ages."

"It really isn't anything to laugh about," he said, but his voice trembled.

"No," agreed Mrs. Mentone, with a like quaver. She drew in a deep breath, and lifted her glass. "Here's to the future!" she said.

"To the future!—long and handsome."

"If it's got pants on that's handsome enough for me," said Mrs. Mentone, and choked on her drink. When she put it down, some of the whisky slopped on the table. She wiped neatly around the glass with her handkerchief.

"Listen," she said, "I don't want to butt in. But what's a man like you want with an old woman? Get yourself a girl with some life in her. You understand, I'm saying this because I've come to think a great deal of you. The world's full of nice women who'd give anything for a little husband and a home of their own. I mean a husband and a little home. You don't have to scrape the bottom of the barrel. Oh, good! We've got some popcorn."

"I don't think you quite understand," he objected. "This is a purely business arrangement. I have in mind a boarding house for students at the university. Naturally, I have to have a place near the transit lines, and not too far from the campus. I was given to understand by a mutual acquaintance that Miss Loyd was anxious to find a buyer. The house is very desirable for my intentions, and I am reluctant to look further until I have definitely ascertained that she and Mrs. Loyd positively will not agree to sell."

He was struck by his remarkable lucidity. Had he left anything out that might color the problem? Try as he would, he could think of nothing more to add that was really relevant. There was the issue. It was a relief to see it stated so plainly.

Certainly, from her silence, Mrs. Mentone was satisfied with the explanation.

"Excuse me a moment," he said.

He got up and crossed the room to a short hallway that had "Gents" painted in black on one of its walls. He looked back briefly. Far away across the dazzling rug Mrs. Mentone appeared, sitting erect in her chair, thoughtfully munching popcorn. She seemed to shimmer a little. He lifted his eyebrows as high as they would go, and blinked his eyes. She vanished altogether into a kaleidoscope of coral and bright red, lavender and gold. He remembered that his glasses hadn't been changed since 1934, and turned and went quickly into the Men's Room.

When he returned, Mrs. Mentone was opening a package of cigarettes, and there were fresh glasses of Scotch at each of their places. He sat down.

Mrs. Mentone thumped her package against the table top, and presently managed to extract a cigarette that was frayed at one end and sadly dented. "Light?" she said, making the request into a dissyllable that carried the hint of a deeper invitation.

The cigarette wavered first upward from her mouth, and then down, and he was obliged to lean far out over the table, and to steady one hand with the other, before he could get the flame under it. He drew away and restored the lighter to his pocket. Mrs. Mentone touched her opulent throat with two brightly lacquered fingernails. The cigarette clung from her lower lip, and a spiral of smoke drifted out of one distended nostril. She looked deeply into his eyes, and the peacock on her bosom rehearsed a series of awkward steps in time to her quick breaths. Mr. Komar looked steadily back, but was presently forced to withdraw his gaze and wipe the tears from his eyes.

"I'm sensitive to smoke," he explained.

"Yes," said Mrs. Mentone somberly. Her lids dropped half across her irises. She took out the cigarette and exhaled a cloud of smoke.

"If Lou could see us now," he said nervously.

Mrs. Mentone abandoned her international manner and gave a ripe snicker. "Wouldn't he *just?* . . ."

"Just what?" he asked roguishly.

Mrs. Mentone waved her hand at him. "Oh, you! You know!"

"I know," he agreed, and the tender, moist sadness drowned him again. "I know." He sighed. "Drink up!" he said.

"Cheers!" cried Mrs. Mentone.

"But, no!" he protested. "This is really serious. Dead serious."

"I *know!* Don't think I don't feel for you—Herbert. May I call you that?"

"You already have."

Her eyelids drooped almost shut. "You've got just about the best line I ever heard."

He smiled—as he fancied—cynically. "It's no line."

"Oh, go on! A man your age? Listen, I'm no metal deflective. Mental defective. Hoo! Get me!"

He took the plump red hand that lay on the table and squeezed it urgently. Mrs. Mentone leapt in her chair and managed at the same time to get her hand fixed more firmly in his grasp. "Ah! Naughty, naughty!" she said. Under the table he felt one of her knees bump against him. She leaned closer; and the heavy aroma of gardenia toilet water struck his nostrils.

His grip relaxed. He wriggled his chair farther away from the table.

Mrs. Mentone instantly cast down her eyes, crushed out her cigarette, took a quick sip from her glass, and became the family friend. "If I can help you in any way at all," she said in a business-like voice, "you need only ask me, Mr. Komar."

He tried desperately to remember what he had hoped she would know.

"If you could tell me," he said slowly, but with a brilliant articulation, "what you know about—*them.* Anything that might clear up this mess."

"Poor mansie." She patted his hand, but quickly withdrew her own into her lap. She shut her eyes for so long that he began to wonder if she'd dropped off to sleep. "Well," she said at last, "we came a year ago; no, more than that now, I guess. I thought right from the beginning there was something funny about the setup. Nothing crooked, I don't mean. But—*queer*. And one day this little kid came to the front door and said was this the haunted house? I thought I'd croak! I said what gave you that notion? and he said that there was an old lady who lived here who was two hundred years old. I said no, not in this house there wasn't, and if I heard he was spreading a story like that around the neighborhood I'd tell his mother. He said I didn't know who his mother was, and I said I could find out, and he said could he look at the witch? and I said young man there is no witch in *this* house; and *then* he said was *I* the witch! and *I* told *him* . . . Well, I'm getting off the tack. Track. Track?"

"Track."

"Yes." She paused thoughtfully. "What was I saying about a track?"

"I don't believe . . ."

"*I* know! But it made me *think*. You know how something will start you thinking? I said to myself—I honestly don't know how this came to me—I said, what if the old woman really isn't so helpless? What about the way she seems to look right through you? What if she can see *perfectly*—and *walk?*"

"Walk!" he exclaimed.

"That's what I thought," nodded Mrs. Mentone emphatically. "Walk, talk. Here's that man again. Well, just a quick one." She smiled guiltily at Mr. Komar. "One for the road, we always say."

Mr. Komar also ordered another Scotch; or perhaps not. At any rate, the barman returned with two.

"What did you find out?" he asked her.

"Pardon?" She was mixing her drink this time, eyes and attention focused on the crisis that the narrow mouth of the glass presented.

"I mean, can she walk?"

"Walk?"

"Mrs. *Loyd!*"

"Oh! *No!* No, I was wrong about that. About her being able to get around, you mean, and see things? No, she's quite helpless."

"I see."

"Absolutely confined to her chair," said Mrs. Mentone sadly. "You know, we even have to lift her onto the– Did you ever notice that chair with the solid bottom?"

"Yes, you told me about that."

"Well, even on to that. It's very tragic. A vigorous woman like her."

"But her wiss are very active," he suggested.

"My God, yes! If I put her on that chair once a day, I do– Oh, wist! Witst! You mean up here?" She tapped her forehead. "Very keen," she agreed with a burble of laughter. "Yes, indeed, sharp as a track."

"Tack."

"You got it," she said approvingly.

"What about . . . what about Blanche?" he asked.

"What about her?"

"Is she–did you suspect her, too?"

Mrs. Mentone took a long swallow. "Blanche," she repeated, licking her lips reflectively. "Who can tell you about Blanche? How can anybody ever know anybody if they don't know themselves?"

"You think Blanche doesn't know herself?"

"Is that what I said?"

"I think so."

"Well, that's what I mean, then."

"You must have noticed *some* things," he said impatiently.

"Noticed, noticed! I've noticed things, all right." She screwed up her face. " 'Annabelle, what did you put in this soup?–*gar*lic?' " Her mimicry was no less cruel for being totally inaccurate. " 'Mother and I are *so* grateful to have Annabelle with us,' she says to their fuddy-duddy friends. As if"–Mrs. Mentone's voice broke–"as if I was a poor relation that was living off them, and they had to be so kind and tolerant. She'll kill you with kindness, that one will: always pretending we're equals. Pre*tend*ing! What the hell's she think she has to pretend for? What's she got so damned much of? What's so fine in her life?—that office downtown? That mausoleum in Grant Street with a ton of mortgage on it? What's there to be kind about? I get paid, don't I? I was brought up just as good as she was, any day, and my folks didn't come from *Canada,* either. Talk about first-generation—she isn't even that!"

"But the family settled first in this country," he replied temperately; "a long time ago."

"Oh, God! Oh, Christ! Long ago! *Long* ago! Is that so fine? By God, I'm sick and fed up with this great lady business. The way she looks at *Lou*—just like he was a fraud and worse. The Mentones had *servants* in *their* home! They had a fine home. It's one of the best funeral parlors in the city now. Do you know after Mother Mentone died they found a check for five thousand dollars in her trunk?—un*cashed!* That's how much money they had! But Lou isn't stuck up about it. Why, when we met he treated me just as nice. . . ."

Her face crumpled up, and tears began to force their way across the red plains of her cheeks.

"This is my best dress," she said, touching the left sleeve and trying vainly to smooth out the wrinkles. "I've had it three years. Do you know how it feels to be that poor?—all the time, pressing in on you. When we came to the Loyds'—well, it was either that or split up and see what we could do alone. Lou never worked in his life until the money ran out, and he's not good for anything even now. Besides, how many places will take a man over forty? Damn few, I'll tell you that. I didn't know what to do, I just didn't know where to turn next." She wiped incautiously at her face, and her rouge smeared her nostrils and chin. "I even thought of turning on the gas—that was when we still had gas left—and us going to bed as usual. Life takes an awful lot of living, doesn't it?" She blew her nose. "Then I saw this ad for a cook and—and a handy man. 'A *couple!*' I cried all night. To end our days as a 'couple'—and Lou so touchy. And it turned out the way life always does, even worse than you expect, and different. I wasn't afraid of the work, and I thought I'd maybe be so glad to have a roof over us and somebody else paying the bills that I'd be able to stomach anything—for a while. But it isn't just for a while. That's what I've learned in Grant Street—now is forever; no change, no hope, go on and on, every day the same, and if it changes it gets worse. He wasn't this way when we were alone together. He'd take me out with him wherever he went. But it's unsettled him—*she's* unsettled him. Oh, yes! I see it. Her cold eyes, and her politeness. 'Lou, would you try to get those screens up before Sunday? I hate to keep after you this way.' 'Lou, I believe the furnace needs fixing.' It's your pride that gets knocked for a loop. I'd never, never let her know that she makes me cry, and it isn't that I care for myself. But why does she have to do it? If she'd even treat me the way the old girl does—you know, about keeping my damn place—I wouldn't mind. You can answer that crap. But not to say *any*thing, and when I do something wrong or Lou lets the fire go out there's never a sharp word. Just the polite little request, over and over until I think I'll scream or take an ax to her. And wouldn't you think she'd be glad to have a man around—I mean, a real *man?* Lou's used to getting a response. What's it do to him—all this perfect breeding?" She shivered and swallowed the last of her drink.

"Well," she said, "that's what I've noticed. You won't get anywhere with her. I don't know what went wrong. I've seen pictures of her when she was young. She was beautiful: she had the kind of beauty that survives the most out-of-date clothes and the craziest hairdresses."

"She's beautiful now," he answered.

"I don't think so. Beauty's love—real beauty is." Her streaked face lifted, and for that moment her conviction illuminated the blurred, ruddy features.

"You've fallen for him all over again."

She laughed awkwardly. "I do that all the time: when he comes home and crawls in beside me, and one of the slats in the bed falls out; when he stands at the sink washing the coal dust off his hands; when I open the hat rack and see his galoshes that he always forgets. . . . I do all the time. That's why, when I can stop . . . stop whatever it is I feel about her, I feel sorry for her."

"And now she's ill."

"Yes." Mrs. Mentone opened her purse and took out a compact. She made hasty repairs with powder, and snapped the compact shut. She looked at him almost with sadness. "But you're not in love with her." Her voice was flat and emphatic.

Though a moment before he would have denied that he had ever considered himself in love with Blanche Loyd, he now felt affronted at her unequivocal certainty.

"I haven't said that I was."

"That's right," she agreed. "You haven't."

"Then, did you—you must have thought I was for a while."

"I guess I thought you were wishing yourself into it."

"What on earth for?"

She shrugged. "You've got to have some reason to stay in."

"That's a funny thing to say."

"I'm tight. Give me time, I'll think of more funny things."

"I'm tight, too," he said; he was torn between astonishment at his admission (which was just true enough to be true, he thought), and pleasure at the extraordinary feeling he had of detachment. He could listen objectively to whatever she might say. "Don't you think I sincerely want to buy a house?"

"No, I don't. You want to buy yourself. You're willing to pay—how much?—nine thousand? ten? for the privilege of owning Herbert Komar free and clear."

"What have I held of him up to now?—first option?"

"How would I know? Maybe you—he—disappeared along about the time middle age set in. Maybe you never noticed he wasn't around until she showed you. I see it so clearly—right now. You're just like Lou: baffled, wondering what's gone wrong or why up to now nothing has ever been right. She's a great one for giving people a perspective. She'll point out all your faults and do her level best to make you suffer for them. But she can't create: she can't even copy what someone else has done."

He thought of Blanche turning away from the parlor window that first night ("It's snowing!" she had cried) and saying, "But there's no good in seeing it when you can't do anything about it." He had thought she meant the snow; he saw now her large reference, saw again that in the act of picking him apart her honesty had made her admit that she knew herself to be no stronger than he was. She was right: there was no use, no use at all.

He pushed back his chair and got up. "I guess we've solved it all," he said. "I'm not in love and I don't want a house."

"I guess we have," Mrs. Mentone agreed, rising.

"All except the problem of myself. What else could I buy, do you suppose?"

She turned at the door of the Ladies' Room where she had left her galoshes and coat.

"Save it for your old age," she said, "and hire a nice couple to look after you."

PART SEVEN

The Happy Rural Seat

· 17 ·

For a week Mr. Komar did nothing more. He took to his dignity as other men take to drink, for refuge and consolation, dropping back gratefully into the old, quiet life. He rejoiced in the close attention that an account called for; even in the fact that his Chevrolet developed a sudden leak in its master cylinder and had to be repaired. On the morning that he left it at the garage he was obliged to take a streetcar to work, and he enjoyed sinking into a wicker seat in the long, lighted car and swaying through the muddy twilight to the subway mouth, where one roared swiftly down into the subterranean dark of the tunnel. It was a great relief to be carried unthinkingly forward: he could have stayed aboard the streetcar, he thought, forever.

On Friday night he had a pleasant evening at Hearts, and he slept late the next morning, so late in fact that Mrs. Hlavaty was given what she assured him was the intense pleasure of having to get another breakfast for him, the eggs from the earlier meal having grown gray, and the toast flinty.

On Sunday afternoon he packed his bags and started east toward the mill town on the state border where he had been going at this season for a good many years to audit the books of one of the firm's regular clients.

He did not return until the following Wednesday.

Of course, he had finished with the Loyds and their attendants: the week of separation, so satisfyingly filled, the tuna fish on the evening of Hearts and the abundant breakfasts he now enjoyed, having muffled up the clamor of Loyd reproaches, protests, evasions. The small trip to the border, he really felt it, did them finally in. He found grotesque and improbable the scene that had occurred that night beside the raw foundation: the spotlight was surely not large or penetrating now, and the whistle hurled at them by the motorist had grown very faint. He could even begin to think about, without a shudder and a mental turning away, his having admitted to Annabelle Mentone that he was "tight." If the statement had been more than a gentlemanly matching of her own confession, it had still been considerably less than the truth. He had not been, he had never been, he would now have no occasion ever to need to be, "tight."

Yes, he was finished with those women: the one with orange hair and red shoes, the one who spilled diamonds on the rug and powder across the dressing table, the one who declared war in a chair before the fire; yes, and with Mary Bush in the portrait, whose eyes were so blue. They had stifled him, he thought, as he drove on toward the city through the darkening and half-familiar countryside, driving, as it seemed to him, with a large, free masculinity (he pushed on the accelerator a little); this clutter of women had stifled him. Mrs. Hlavaty and Mildred Kasco were part of the clutter, too, and—affirming as it struck him they did all that Blanche Loyd rejected and deplored—even Sadie and his poor, dead mother. For his part, he rejected and deplored the lot of them.

Let the cat, he thought indifferently, keep possession of her grubby wainscotting. The mouse would back away, back down, run away into the fields. How could he have let so many women sweep across him, push him around? War to the death. Their proclamations came back to him. *If it were only to the death! There's nothing for you here. Treating my home like a tourist camp! You want to get out of yourself, Herbert.* And two of them, silent but obtrusive, brightly watching him from their opposite, their opposing spheres: his mother and Mary Bush. How they ranged around him in the little car, and as he burrowed into the dingy city they seemed to take on substance, so that coming out of a shabby bar was a figure not unlike Mrs. Mentone's; and as he passed the lighted façade of a bus Blanche Loyd turned her face away from the window.

Well, let them haunt him. He could deal with their spectres, he who had none of his own. In time they would flicker and die before his steady resolve. In time he would be able to decide, quite objectively, about the possibility of getting a house for himself; in the country around Yellow Center, perhaps. After all, was sixty the time to start a new enterprise? Was it not rather the time for nailing up the gate, putting the car on blocks, getting, even as Annabelle Mentone had ironically suggested, a nice couple in? In ten years . . . why, he thought, in ten years I may be helpless, or in fifteen, or twenty. It was a large expectation that would bank on twenty.

He turned into his own street. It was eight o'clock, and the street had that front-of-the-house look that indicates the evening is moving on. Parties have begun, baby sitters been left with instructions and clean diapers, the dishes are washed, the furnace fixed until bedtime. The radio is on, the newspaper almost read. It is the looked forward to, invariably empty, inbetween time of the inbetween season.

He left his car in the front of the drive while he got out his suitcases and took them up on the front porch. As he set them down and reached for his key, the porch light came on and the door opened.

"Here he is!" said Mrs. Hlavaty, and though he could see no one behind her in the vestibule or the hall, it was apparent that she was speaking to someone else.

She held the door open, and he stooped and picked up a bag in each hand. "Back again," he said. In the hall he met Miss Kasco, who had just come from the living room.

"*Here* he is!" she, too, called.

"Here I am," he agreed. "You must have heard me drive in."

He put down the two cases and pulled off his gloves.

"I should think so," replied Miss Kasco. "We've been waiting hours, it seems."

"I told you he'd come, Mildred," said Mrs. Hlavaty, shutting the door.

"Yes, you were certain; I know. I was just nervous. After the effort it must have been to *get* here," she added obscurely. "And it was getting so late."

He looked at the two women, baffled and a little annoyed. There was an evident current of excitement running between them. He tried to think what it was reminiscent of, and he remembered the rare times when Mrs. Hlavaty's brother from Johnstown called her and said he was coming out to the house. Mr. Hlavaty's brother was the ornament of the family, and his periodic brief appearances in the city, always unannounced, brought into the house a breath of a world equally remote from all of them, a world of country clubs, fine cars, good clothes. At these times Mrs. Hlavaty always whisked nervously around, picking up newspapers and magazines, emptying ashtrays, dusting end tables, and Miss Kasco rushed to her room and descended presently in whatever was her current best dress. For a night and a day the household wore this precise air of subdued excitement, of delight, more especially of awe, that he now observed in it.

He said, turning to Mrs. Hlavaty (who unexpectedly took his overcoat from him), "I told you I probably wouldn't be in before now."

"Well," said Miss Kasco loudly (again he felt she was addressing someone unseen), "I'll just run along up." She added, as if in an attempt somehow to make herself part of the brilliance of the scene, "I have a simply marvelous book for you, if you want it, Mr. Komar. I'll put it on your bed."

"Come down and have a cup of coffee later, Mildred," called Mrs. Hlavaty, her voice, too, heavy with the meaning that Mr. Komar could not grasp. She turned to him. "You go right on in, Mr. Komar."

He looked blankly at her. "In? Where? Has your brother come?"

She now laughed in the gay and social way that he never heard except when her brother was present (then, it always seemed to him, everything, each simplest remark, struck her as singularly deserving of her mirth).

"Why, just in *there!*" she said, and she flourished his coat toward the living room.

When he still hesitated, she took his arm firmly and marched him along before her through the archway.

"*Here* he is at last!" she cried, and she gave him a push.

"Mrs. *Loyd!*"

Lily Loyd looked toward him from a chair in front of the fireplace. The red light behind the artificial logs played across her face and gave it a look of quite unnatural good health.

She half put out her arm toward him, but as he stood rooted to the carpet some distance from her she presently dropped it again.

"Mrs. Loyd," he repeated more slowly.

He looked around the room. Except for himself and the two women, it was empty. There was no Blanche in evidence, no solicitous Mrs. Mentone. It was quite as if the old woman had descended, ponderously but, no doubt, with dignity, through the Spanish plaster ceiling. She was dressed (even in his shock and bewilderment he noted so much) magnificently, in a silk dress that was deeply violet. Its collar was made of a heavy white satin, and the large cuffs were satin, too. She wore the pearls that he remembered from her photograph—the great rope slung round her neck and dropping across the white satin into the purple shadows of her lap. In her ears were tiny diamond hoops. Positively, in the subdued light, she shimmered and glittered, largely there, and very, he thought, taking a step toward her, overwhelming.

"Well!" Mrs. Hlavaty threw her small ejaculation hopefully into the silence, but it dropped far down and was lost.

Presently, even her curiosity gave way before the appalling tension of the moment, and she said, "I'll just run upstairs with your coat, Mr. Komar. Excuse me, Mrs. Loyd."

She retreated into the hall, and he heard her steps mounting rapidly. A moment later the door of his bedroom opened and her heavy tread reverberated across the ceiling.

Lily Loyd once more raised her hand (he saw a diamond mounted in heavy gold on it: a man's ring), and this time he did move toward her. He took the dry, crooked fingers hesitantly. Her own grip was stronger. In fact, she gave his hand a quick squeeze, and for an instant it almost seemed to him that she was laughing.

"Have you been waiting long?" he asked.

"I have been very pleasantly entertained."

"I see. Well . . . I'm glad they've made you—comfortable." He did not know what to do with her hand. Flushing deeply, he laid it back in her lap.

"You are very careful of other people's property," she said amusedly. He was no more ready with a reply than he had been with an appropriate gesture. Indeed, his little stock of remarks and attitudes, so weathered and sure, seemed all of them unfitted to the occasion. He could not have been more unprepared if his own mother had risen suddenly from her grave and come and taken the chair opposite Lily Loyd, in which he now, weakly, sat down. Nor could he have been more dismayed.

"That woman will not be able to contain herself very long," continued Mrs. Loyd.

"Mrs. Hlavaty?" he asked, grateful that they should begin with such a familiar theme.

"Is that how one says it? I have mumbled at her: I didn't want the poor woman to know that I found it impossible to contort my tongue adequately. Yes, that one, and the other—with the sharp nose."

He gave a shout of laughter. "But how would you know?" he asked.

The question did not seem to her, as indeed he had not intended it to be, cruel. "There is a peculiar physiognomy for every humour."

"Humour?"

"Miss Kasco's humour is incessant curiosity. I believe she is a scholar: she seems to love knowledge for its own sake. I admire a scholar: I have filled her up."

"Humour," he said again. "Yes, that's good for it. That's just what there is about her. She teaches," he added, under the impression that the information was somehow relevant, "in the high school."

Mrs. Loyd nodded. "Civics," she said. "And she belongs to the Literary Guild, which she tells me distributes the very best in current literature. She also tells me she is forty-three years old, though her friends won't believe it, and a native of East Liverpool, Ohio—a fact she finds difficult to believe herself. She began her teaching career in Indiana, but left after a tragic romance with the superintendent, which ended when he married the head of the school cafeteria."

Mr. Komar was silent.

"She thinks you are quite the gentleman," Mrs. Loyd added with a grunt; "but that you don't give a girl much . . ." Her voice trailed off.

"Much what?" he asked fiercely.

"Much of whatever it is a man gives a girl."

"Forty-three!" he said, half in surprise, half by way of explaining why it was he gave nothing.

"And Blanche," observed Mrs. Loyd, "is fifty-six."

"Miss Kasco does not own a house," he retorted.

"Well, well," replied Mrs. Loyd, "neither does Blanche."

"Miss Kasco has a pointed nose," he said defensively.

Mrs. Loyd chuckled, and he observed a note of pride in her voice when she said, "And my daughter has not?"

"You should know," he answered shortly.

"Mrs. Hlavaty, on the other hand," she imperturbably continued, "thinks that still water runs deep. Mrs. Hlavaty has had a good deal of experience with still water, she gives me to believe. It's the mouse, she says, with more sense than consistency, that always gets the cheese."

"The traps laid for me are all empty ones," he said, and was pleased to think that he had stung her, for she did not reply at once.

"And now," she presently said, after the silence in which her fingers had played with the rope of pearls, "I come with still another empty trap, so you are quite right."

"How did you come at all?" he asked, for he had begun to wonder whether Mrs. Mentone's wild speculation that the old woman could walk when she chose to was correct.

"Louis Mentone brought me in a cab," she said, "and your friends kindly helped him bring me indoors. Of course, they have been expecting me since Monday night."

"You called?" he asked.

"I called in desperation, and that is what brought me to you as soon as you returned. I thought you would not come again to us."

"No," he answered.

"I dare say Annabelle finished whatever it was that Blanche began."

"She was kind about it," he said.

"We are all so kind."

"Not Blanche. I thought once she was, but now—"

"Even my daughter. It is our great fault that we are kind indiscriminately—I to you, to myself, to Blanche; you to yourself, to Blanche, to me"—she added slyly—"to Mrs. Hlavaty. Only Miss Kasco seems to be rejected from the earthly bliss."

"You omit Blanche except as recipient," he pointed out.

"She is the light," her mother replied. "From her flow the currents that prick us into reluctant life."

"Then she is kindest to herself," he said bitterly.

"No," rejoined Mrs. Loyd at once, "she is not. She is very hard on herself. She can be indifferent to nothing, that is her failing. I love her, and if I were not so old and if I were that kind of mother, I would cry for her. Still, I *am* her mother; and now I will be honest in her fashion. I will tell you that I come to use you once more, and that I am on her side. Poor old man!" she cried suddenly, gently, "you'll get no mercy from us!"

"I don't ask for mercy."

"Or sympathy," she added boldly.

He shrugged. "I'll get through."

She slumped a little in her chair. "Then that is more than I shall do."

And he was honest, too. "Yes," he said softly. At that, she pulled herself erect once more.

"My daughter," she went on, turning her brilliant, bleak gaze directly on him, "has gone."

Blanche was dead. He felt his cheeks go flat against his jaws, and an acid saliva run in his mouth. He felt bitterly used up; he thought he ought to give sympathy: he wanted only to ask it. "The doll," was all he said. He sat back in his chair and closed his eyes that stung.

Mrs. Loyd, with what he took later to be intent, let him enjoy his misconstruction for a long minute, in which, to say the truth, he did thrill and then go cold, could have wept, but did not know for what.

"When?" he presently put to her.

"Sunday night on the train."

"I see." He saw at once, and resolved to give Lily Loyd no satisfaction in her mischief. "To Canada?"

"To the house."

"The happy rural seat?" he brought out ironically.

She looked surprised. "The family home," she amended. "She could not turn to me. She had nowhere else to turn."

"To Mary Bush."

"Mary Bush is dead," said Mrs. Loyd flatly.

"Never dead," he affirmed with equal flatness. "Never so much alive as now."

Mrs. Loyd laughed. "Well, you are a romancer."

"Alive in *you*," he said firmly, "and haunting *her*."

"You've fallen in love with a portrait."

"I see the portrait in life."

"You mean? . . ."

"I mean, you."

"Well," admitted Mrs. Loyd, "Mary Bush was stubborn. She was a curmudgeon."

"I said too much," he went on, "for she had faith. She wouldn't have got lost in side issues. She wasn't afraid to take her own tack."

"She sailed close to the wind," agreed Mrs. Loyd.

"You're very amicable," he said, surprised, remembering her earlier fierceness.

"Why not? Mary Bush is very dead. You'll get no help from her."

"I have had from her all the help I want," he replied. "I see the sails furled, the ballast thrown out. I see the same ship before me right at this moment, but the rigging's gone, there'll never be another cargo. That's what Mary Bush has taught me."

"I am flattered," replied Lily Loyd. "I take it I am at least a three-masted schooner. My daughter, I suppose, is the Flying Dutchman?"

"Well," he said, but he was obliged to laugh, "*is* it so far off?"

"*I* am not afraid."

"Not for yourself," he agreed.

"And you?" she asked, turning it on him.

"Well, and what of me?"

"I take it you are the rat gnawing away at the hull. In your ignorance you do not understand that you will scuttle both us and yourself."

"There's no mercy there!" he agreed. "I gave you a nobler berth."

"I am a larger affair," she pointed out. "In me," she said rather ponderously, "you exist."

"That's an outrageous thing to say."

She replied calmly, "The whole undertaking's outrageous."

"Do you think I am afraid?" he asked, reverting to what they had broken off from a moment earlier.

"Don't you think you are?" she asked with apparent astonishment.

"What am I afraid of?"

"Why," she returned, "of yourself. You nibble away, making a larger and larger nothing into which you'll finally disappear."

"Not I," he replied firmly. "I've—if a poor rat can do it—washed my hands of it. I've drawn back. I've jumped ashore."

They heard footsteps coming down the stairs, and their conversation broke off. He saw positive anguish in Mrs. Loyd's face; having said so much, she had evidently, she had quite surely, not said what she came for. But the steps, after what seemed to the listeners a slight hesitation, moved through the doorway from the hall into the dining room, and then into the kitchen. Mr. Komar heard the metallic thump and splash that meant the tap at the kitchen sink had been turned on.

"Then," said Mrs. Loyd, leaning toward him earnestly, and once again extending her hand (piteously, a little to the right of where he actually sat), "then, come back. You have done too much not to do a little more."

"I've done what you asked," he answered hardly. "I put it to her, and it was just as you knew it would be. She backed down." He groaned. "If she had really done that! She only did nothing. She only staved me off. It was a clear victory for you."

"Help me to gain completely, then," said the old woman.

"You have; you've shut yourselves up."

"She's *gone!*" Lily Loyd cried.

He now took in absolutely, and for the first time, the sense of it, but he was struck most by the fact of its being a clear victory for him: they were, in their ways, two victors. Lily Loyd had driven him out; but he had driven out Blanche Loyd. "Well," he replied, "you still have the house."

The old woman flinched, but she answered bravely enough. "You'd not say that to Mary Bush."

"She'd not make such an unreasonable request. She'd stick to her guns."

Mrs. Loyd ran her hand anxiously across the chair arm. "What time is it?" she asked.

He glanced at the mantel clock. "Almost nine."

"That foolish woman will be with us in a minute." She closed her eyes and leaned her white head against the back of the chair. "I would like to go home."

He said, defensively, "I could do nothing by coming back. I would only make the hole a little deeper. I would side with her against you, and she with you against me. We would be exactly where we began. I don't want a house, any house, as much as that. I especially don't *not* want your house to such a degree. I have," he brought it out proudly, "withdrawn. I ask no one's help."

"But if you did?" she asked urgently. "If you did?"

"I wouldn't expect to get it," he said sternly.

"I don't ask to help *you*," she pointed out. "I ask you to help me. How shall we do anything if we all withdraw?"

"But," he said, "it is just nothing that you required."

"I see now we've done too much, though, to stop here," she repeated.

"I can't grasp your love of a house; but then," he went on, "I am a foreigner."

"We've been in it," she vaguely replied, "constantly."

"I was for years constantly in Lark Street," he answered.

"We brought everything into it," she said, "everything from

over there. Right into it. Even those old pure selves. It saw our rise and decline, and reflected both."

"The house is still another self," he said facetiously, but she took him up at once.

"Yes! One belonging to all of us. It's something," she went on, "to grow old in a house."

"Whereas I have grown old in many houses," he said, "and none of them my own. And my mother," he went on grimly, "died in a Home for the Aged. She was very foreign," he said angrily. "At the end she couldn't speak a word of English. It's lucky she had no fine feelings."

They heard a rattle of cups and saucers being taken from the dining room china closet. Mrs. Loyd this time made no urgent movement. She sank deeper into the chair, and even the rosy glow of the electric logs could not now bring any bloom to her exhausted face.

"I know nothing of your mother," she replied finally.

"Well," he said, "and there it is. I know nothing of you."

But his compassion was too great to allow of this flat conclusion, as it certainly seemed to be (he heard the coffee pot scrape across the iron grating of the stove, and knew the end was at hand). "What will you do?" he asked.

"Do? I'll do nothing. What," she asked, perplexed, "would I 'do'?"

"She won't stay long," he said. "There's you, there's her business. . . ."

"It isn't her staying I came to see you about. It's the way she comes back."

"Why," he said ingenuously, "she'll be all rested. . . ."

"Ready for the long sleep. Ah!" she cried. "I didn't want *that!*"

They heard a great rattling and trampling as Mrs. Hlavaty came through the kitchen door.

"What would *I* do?" he asked quickly.

"Bring her!" said Mrs. Loyd. Her crooked fingers gripped the arms of the chair until he saw the upholstery indent under her nails. "Tell her you love her. Oh!" she flung out. "We could fight it from there–gloriously!"

"I don't know. . . ." He floundered still as he saw Mrs. Hlavaty approach across the darkness of the dining room, a tray borne nobly aloft in her hands.

"We'd sail again," said Lily Loyd, in a whisper so strong he was certain it was carried to Mrs. Hlavaty's startled ears. "Close to the wind!"

"The three of us," he said.

Only a moment did she hesitate, then she positively affirmed, "The three of us."

"I couldn't leave right away," he said hastily; "not before Saturday morning."

"You'll do it?" she asked eagerly.

"Coffee! Coffee!" announced Mrs. Hlavaty. "Oh," she went on, setting the tray on the coffee table, "I wish you could see my girl friend's African violets that I was telling you about, Mrs. Loyd. She's got her dining room lit right now, and they're just a vision of heaven."

"I'll do it!" he told her loudly.

"My housekeeper has such good luck with violets," said Lily Loyd. "I'll get her to give you some slips. Coffee, did you say? Isn't this a pleasant surprise!"

· 18 ·

"AND so naturally I thought," continued Mrs. Hlavaty (she had sustained this monologue for many minutes together), "*what* is he up to? You can understand my feeling, Mrs. Loyd. A woman is so defenseless; she needs propping. Mr. Komar has propped so beautifully all these years, and when he turned his face against me (try some of those walnut cookies, Mrs. Loyd. My secret pal made them for me; we have a little club, you know—just some of us girls who grew up together—and we give each other presents; I'll find out who she is at our Christmas party; well, I really know already—it's Agnes Koch, Mildred, you remember her—the one who had everything taken out of her last spring) I just felt as if my last prop had been"—she paused dramatically; also, for breath—"*ripped*"—she brought out—"right from under me. I was telling Mr. Komar that I laid awake half the night, worried sick. Mildred felt it too, didn't you, Mildred?"

Thus appealed to, Miss Kasco assented so vigorously that her paper napkin slid to the floor. "Oh, yes, I felt it too!"

"We all felt it," said Mrs. Hlavaty. She smiled warmly at Mr. Komar. "It wasn't like a family any more," she added.

"Our man around the house!" exclaimed Miss Kasco, tucking her napkin into her belt and smiling at the happy phrase.

"Yes, suddenly for him *not* to be around! More coffee, Mrs. Loyd?"

"Just half a cup, please," said Lily Loyd.

"Well, aren't you a funny one! Still, two half cups make a whole one. I suppose it stays hotter longer that way, doesn't it? Or would it?" She appealed to the group. "Would half a cup stay hotter longer than a whole cup?"

"My housekeeper," said Lily Loyd, nipping this interesting speculation in the bud, "says I spill it if I get too much at once." She extended her cup uncertainly toward Mrs. Hlavaty.

"Isn't that funny?" Mrs. Hlavaty once more appealed to Mr. Komar and Miss Kasco as she filled the cup carefully to the half-way mark. "Aren't servants funny?" she amended.

"She is hardly a servant," replied Mrs. Loyd. "Thank you. She reminds me every day that she is just as good as I am."

"Isn't that marvelous?" cried Mrs. Hlavaty. "I suppose she's a wonderful type?"

"*You* tell us, Mr. Komar," said Miss Kasco archly. "Is she that?"

"Well, she's wonderful," he replied.

"I'm sure she could learn a great deal from Mrs. Loyd," said Mrs. Hlavaty. "Such lovely manners . . . Here, Mrs. Loyd, let me put one of these cookies in your hand; they're not very crumbly. My washwoman is that way too: so funny. A great fat Negro. Aren't they funny?"

"Oh, *she's* a type," affirmed Miss Kasco. "I just want to die at her accent. She gets me talking that way if I'm around long. She asked me once if I came from the South, and I thought I'd split. I said, yes, South *Ohio!* Well, she said she'd never have guessed. Of course, we're very near the border down there. I've lost all my accent, but it used to be quite different. And I must say my sympathies are all with the South. If we had another war I think I'd march right down to Richmond."

"Oh, *wouldn't* you?" agreed Mrs. Hlavaty. "Heaven knows I don't believe in slavery. Well, you can see what it's like right in Europe now. But what are you going to do with them? Pass me his cup, will you, Mildred? Minnie's so different, though, don't you think, Mildred?"

"My goodness, I should say so," agreed Miss Kasco. "She's a widow, Mrs. Loyd, with two dear little boys. And a very devout Baptist."

"I think someone like that deserves a lot of credit," said Mrs. Hlavaty. "There you are, Mr. Komar. Give him the sugar, Mildred. But still and *all* . . ." she went on, apparently qualifying the generous democracy her affection for the admirable Minnie called forth.

"Well, well," said Lily Loyd reflectively, "I've noticed how the mind moves in these divided tracks even among," she hesitated, and then concluded with what struck Mr. Komar as a rather terrifying deliberation, "even among ourselves."

Mr. Komar held his breath, but the intent of the old woman's remark escaped her other two hearers.

"If you mean the hunkies, *yes*," said Miss Kasco promptly. "At least the colored people know their place."

"We're very fortunate on this block," said Mrs. Hlavaty. "Really high-grade people. Of course, we're a churchy neighborhood. Almost everybody goes to the cathedral over south of here: quite a well-to-do congregation. It discourages that other element, I think. I always tell Mildred that the day I see the money falling off in our collection plate, I'll know it's time to sell the house."

"You've lived here a long time?" asked Mrs. Loyd.

"Since I was married. Let's see, twenty-two . . . no; twenty-three years!"

"That's quite a time," agreed the old woman.

"Too long," Mrs. Hlavaty asserted. "My brother and his wife move every year or so, and I really think they've got the right idea. Why tie yourself down so? A house this size is just ridiculous for one woman, like me; even when Fred was still here it was too big. That's why we took in guests, originally. I won't say the money isn't very welcome to me now, things being as skimpy as they've been these last years. But sometimes I think it's more like the house owning you. My niece and her husband bought a place recently that has all anybody needs. They've got a nice dining alcove at one end of the living room, and a second floor they can finish off if they ever need more than the two bedrooms. And there's ground enough at the side of the lot for a porch if they want one. Now, isn't that sensible?"

"It sounds—*very* sensible," said Lily Loyd. "I suppose," she went on, "they do everything together?"

Mrs. Hlavaty looked puzzled. "They're never apart," she said finally, "except the night Eugene goes bowling." Her face cleared. "I see! I hadn't thought of it before, but a small house keeps people together, doesn't it? Besides, families are smaller these days; people don't need so much space. Anyway, who can afford the upkeep?"

Lily Loyd nodded. "Money does always come into it." She twisted the rope of pearls in her lap.

"But for people who have *house*keepers! . . ." cried Miss Kasco.

"Oh, yes!" agreed Mrs. Hlavaty. "Housekeepers make the difference."

"That is the distinction?" asked Lily Loyd. "That's what separates the various tracks?"

Mrs. Hlavaty piled the cups together on the tray. "Why, yes," she said, "housekeepers; and what you just said: money. That's all the difference, isn't it?"

"Among . . . among *our* kind?" Mrs. Loyd prodded.

Mrs. Hlavaty laughed. "Oh, of course, only among 'our kind.' "

Mr. Komar shut his eyes briefly: the room swarmed with the ugly words and their uglier, their compelling, implications.

"You parcel them all up too," he said weariedly.

"Parcel what?" inquired Miss Kasco.

"People—everyone," he answered.

Mrs. Hlavaty smiled rigidly. "You wouldn't raise a rumpus, of course, if I rented that room next to yours to some colored man."

"Oh," he agreed, "I'd make a row."

"*Well*, then . . ."

"*Men!*" said Miss Kasco tolerantly. "They talk so big, but just take them at their word once . . ." She blushed, and there was a small silence while the whole group recollected the sad defection of Miss Kasco's superintendent of schools.

"We're shifty," agreed Mr. Komar, to cover her embarrassment.

"And women are too hasty," said Mrs. Hlavaty generously. "Look at me—thinking all kinds of things about you—Herbert. May I call you that?—though I'll feel a little funny after all these years."

"Everybody does," he answered dryly.

"Herbert, Herbert," repeated Miss Kasco. "May I have that privilege?"

"Go ahead," he told her.

"And I," she said, "am Mildred. Isn't that stuffy of me? At home I never answered to anything except Milly—and I had a nickname, but don't think you'll tease *that* out of me!"

"Now, wait a minute!" said Mrs. Hlavaty. "Honestly, I meant what I said; I sinned in my mind against you, Herbert. But you were too generous to tell us what you were up to. Wasn't it generosity, Mrs. Loyd?—to *you*, I mean."

"He is unfailingly generous," agreed Lily Loyd, nor did he detect any irony in her response. She looked very white, very tired; and her old hand shook as she lifted it and adjusted an earring. She glimmered, she shone, she bloomed with purple and white, but he felt that the regalia was empty: the monarch had departed.

"I know it!" said Mrs. Hlavaty. "And I'm so glad we've had this chance to get things straight." She turned to Mr. Komar. "Mrs. Loyd has told us everything."

"She has?" he repeated dully.

"It's so splendid of you," said Miss Kasco. "So splendid for all of us just to *feel* you. And so beautiful, too, for you to help Mrs. Loyd this way."

He looked sharply at the old woman, but her face registered only her great fatigue.

"I do what I can," he replied vaguely. "Does *she?*" he asked, glancing once more at Lily Loyd. "Does she tell you how she helps me?"

"There's the beauty of it, of course," said Mrs. Hlavaty. "She can only do what *you* will do for her."

"She can do nothing for herself," Miss Kasco assured him.

"It's all so delicate," Mrs. Hlavaty added.

And Miss Kasco cried, "Poor *thing!*"

He looked at her blankly. "Mrs. Loyd?"

"Oh, no!" said Mrs. Hlavaty, before Miss Kasco could reply. "Her daughter."

"My bewildered daughter," said Lily Loyd.

"Ah!" he exclaimed. "Your bewildered daughter." He looked at her expectantly, forgetting that she could never interpret a glance. "You told them? . . ."

"Oh, everything," said Lily Loyd firmly.

Everything? About his desire for a house? about himself?—and Blanche?

"You told them about—Miss Loyd?" he inquired tentatively.

"Poor thing!" Mrs. Hlavaty once more exclaimed, and from the compassion in her voice he judged that Lily Loyd's "everything" had, in fact, comprised very little. "I know just what got into her. I've wanted to go off that way myself—oh, a hundred times. You know what I said to you just the other day, Mr.—Herbert?"

"Yes, indeed," he agreed, "just the other day."

"If anyone can clear it up, *you* can," Miss Kasco told him.

"Our captain," said Lily Loyd.

The other ladies laughed a great deal at this image, even while they assented. "An—an admiral!" proposed Mrs. Hlavaty, plumbing uncertainly the fishy vocabulary.

"An admiral with an account book," added Miss Kasco.

"An *ad*mirable account book," suggested Lily Loyd.

During the small hilarity Mr. Komar began just to get the drift of things. "Their finances," he said.

"*Such* a problem for all of us," remarked Mrs. Hlavaty sympathetically, "and for ladies of the old school—oh! Impossible! My grandmother, I remember: she was from the old country—they were very good people there, and she could not, she *could* not get the hang of taking care of money. She went away finally, just as your daughter has, Mrs. Loyd—only not so far. My grandfather found her walking the streets, crying her eyes out. She couldn't find twenty dollars. It was a great sum in those days, you understand. They ran it to earth finally, in a bureau drawer, under one of her garments. After that, grandfather gave her what she needed when she needed it, and they simply threw away the little book she'd been making her entries in."

"Dear me," said Lily Loyd, with every appearance of sadness, "if it were only a case of our having mislaid it!"

"Don't we know!" said Miss Kasco. "But if anyone can straighten you out, Herbert can."

"He has done so much already," said Lily Loyd.

"Just his presence does something, doesn't it?" asked Mrs. Hlavaty. "We feel it here, you know, too. That's why I was so upset—that's hardly strong enough for what I felt—when I thought he was giving us up. But of course I see now—his very virtue kept him from telling us the real case. But without that virtue? . . ."

"Yes, indeed," said Lily Loyd, "without *that*, he could hardly have done for us at all."

"I hope," he here said sharply, "to persuade Mrs. Loyd to sell her house."

"Naughty man!" said Miss Kasco. "She told us that, you know! But we understand quite well that things are still very far from *that* pass." She appeared to reflect on the still considerable affluence suggested by a housekeeper.

"Did she tell you that she had had an offer?" he pursued.

"She said she had been badgered to death," replied Miss Kasco. "And badgered to death by *you!*" she surprisingly went on.

"By me!" he exclaimed. Again he looked at Lily Loyd.

"Oh, yes, we know how much you want her to sell. But we agree with her: you go too far."

"I go too far!" he echoed.

"If you had ever had a home," said Mrs. Hlavaty, "you'd know how Mrs. Loyd feels. *I* do," she added.

"You suddenly favor sentiment over sense," he pointed out.

"Sense can go too far," she assured him. "Mrs. Loyd hopes you'll find some other solution for her. Well, she'll have told you that herself—here tonight."

"She's said something like that," he agreed.

"I'm sure," Lily Loyd informed the other ladies, "that Mr. Komar thinks me a muddle-headed and sentimental old woman."

"And so you should be!" cried Mrs. Hlavaty. "Sentiment is beautiful—beautiful and precious. We mustn't be too clear-sighted," she said.

"Well," he in his turn assured her, "I'm not clear-sighted."

From the warm gaze that Mrs. Hlavaty and Miss Kasco turned on him, he felt certain that this demur, too, however untruthful they believed it to be, was taken by them as springing out of his great virtue. He gave up the struggle. Lily Loyd had made the situation so clear to them that the real truth would merely confuse matters—so much so, that a more extravagant illusion of his virtue would come forth; indeed, he almost felt that for him to assert now that it was he who wanted the house would make them more lively in their assurance that his generosity had practically no bounds. What lengths, they would exclaim, would he not go to for an aged lady?

He said, "You understand that I'll have to go away at the end of this week? To the—to Canada."

"We are with you all the way," Mrs. Hlavaty said. She leaned far over and patted his much-patted arm.

"All the way!" Miss Kasco echoed, and barely restrained herself from echoing the gesture, too.

"We will be waiting," Mrs. Hlavaty added.

"And I shall be waiting," said Lily Loyd.

"And I suppose Miss Loyd is waiting—over there," he said.

"All waiting," agreed Miss Kasco. "It is up to *you*."

Here the doorbell rang.

"That will be? . . ." began Mrs. Hlavaty, getting up.

"My housekeeper," supplemented Lily Loyd. "She told me she'd give me until ten. No later."

Miss Kasco at once set up a laugh, but she was left this time to relish alone the tyranny of servants, for Mrs. Hlavaty had gone briskly into the hall.

"She's here! She's quite well!" they heard her buoyantly cry. "We've taken good care of her—you'll see you could trust us, after all."

Then Mrs. Mentone was in the room, followed by a taxi driver.

"Well, Mother? . . ." she began.

"Mother!" whispered Miss Kasco in an appreciative side tone.

"This is Miss Kasco," Mrs. Hlavaty was saying; "and I am Pauline Hlavaty." Mrs. Mentone smiled briefly at her and Miss Kasco. "Mr. Komar of course you know."

"Mr. Komar," repeated Mrs. Mentone frigidly.

"Good evening," he replied.

"I'll just get Mrs. Loyd's things," said Mrs. Hlavaty. "They're in the hall closet."

"Are you all right?" asked Mrs. Mentone, stooping in front of the old woman and examining her face anxiously.

"Oh, she's fine!" said Miss Kasco.

Mrs. Mentone ignored her. "You're not too tired?"

"I've had a beautiful evening," Lily Loyd said, and she contrived somehow to look directly at Mr. Komar. "We will be able to go ahead now."

"I leave you to worry about that," said Mrs. Mentone brusquely. "If we can only get home . . ."

Mrs. Hlavaty returned with an enormous black coat over her arm, and a curious hat, like a dishpan that someone had sat on, in her hand. "Mildred," she said, "could you get the chair? The one we brought her in on. I left it in the dining room."

Miss Kasco at once departed, with such speed and intent that one might have thought she was late for a conference with the principal. During her absence, Mrs. Hlavaty helped Lily Loyd to lean forward while Mrs. Mentone slipped the old woman's arms into the bulky coat and planted the crumpled dishpan on her head. Thus swathed, she almost disappeared from sight. Miss Kasco returned with a light wicker porch chair with arms, and into this Mrs. Loyd was placed through the combined efforts of Mrs. Mentone, the taxi man, and Mrs. Hlavaty. Mr. Komar hovered just outside the little group, unconsciously trying to look as if he were helping. Lily Loyd looked very ill when her attendants had finally got her settled, and her eyes were closed.

Occasionally, her tongue slipped out and ran along her lips, but he saw that those thin lips were dry as ever when the tongue receded.

"Are you ready, Mother?" Mrs. Mentone asked presently, in a voice that died to a whisper on the last syllables for lack of breath.

"I'm ready," announced Lily Loyd.

"Then . . ." Mrs. Mentone motioned to the taximan to take one side of the chair. She herself bent down to grasp the other, and now Mr. Komar did come forward.

"Let me do that," he said, and he tried, gently, to brush her aside.

She stood upright and glared at him. "I'll do it!" she said. "I can do *that* for her!"

He stepped back, and it was in this way that he had his odd, brief vision, shaped, it surely must have been, he thought later, by the imaginings of his romantic youth: of Lily Loyd bumping across the living room carpet, her earrings catching the light and glittering against her somber black, her hand now and again lifting so that the diamond there, too, flashed and winked. Across the tropical rug she progressed, over the woven jungle flowers and the yellow temples, like a—like a what? Standing idle and curiously isolated beside the coffee table with its pile of cups and plates, he sought back. Like an empress, he thought, borne in her open sedan chair through the conquered but still alien territory. That is what he thought. Yes, Lily Loyd had unflinchingly invaded, she had planted whatever an empress would plant in the strange new territory: her flag, her seal. Now she was borne out into the night of the farther, the darker adventure they both knew awaited her, and her regalia of conquest, her diamonds blinking, her old felt crown, asserted the challenge behind them that she was too tired any longer to command from herself. The empress was an old, old lady.

Yes, he at last gave her that credit, nor did he begrudge it: she was a lady. She had a lady's arrogance, but she had more, she had her beautiful bravery.

And he thought it was beautiful, seeing her this way, crossing the cold jungle accompanied only by her little court of one.

At the archway this court abruptly gave out. Mrs. Mentone let down her side of the chair and straightened her back painfully. She turned to Mr. Komar, and he saw that her eyes were light with tears.

"I can't!" she said. "I can't do even this for her. I can't!" She turned away.

Lily Loyd put up her hand once more, as if to steel her faltering maid, or perhaps to comfort her, but Mrs. Mentone had gone ahead into the hall and now stood with her hand on the vestibule door, her back still toward them.

Mr. Komar went over to the chair and bent down. Together he and the taximan got the old woman out on the porch and slowly, agonizingly, down the front steps and over to the cab door. Here, once more, she was lifted from the wicker chair and—there was no other way to do it—literally stuffed into the front seat of the cab. Her hat fell over her face, and one of the gloves she had held tightly in her right hand dropped onto the running board. Mr. Komar stooped over and picked it up and gave it back to her, glad for once of her blindness: she could not see the tears in his eyes. He straightened her hat clumsily, aware of Mrs. Mentone's fierce and jealous eyes on his back. Then, gently, he closed the cab door; the driver got in at the other side, and Mrs. Mentone climbed into the rear seat.

"If you'll wait," he said, "until I get my coat, I'll . . ."

"There's no need," replied Mrs. Mentone. "Lou's home. He'll help." She slammed her door.

The motor whirled and started. Behind him, on the lighted porch, Mr. Komar heard Mrs. Hlavaty and Miss Kasco talking. As the taxi began to glide backward down the drive, he picked up the wicker chair and started toward them. They were both waving now, and Mrs. Hlavaty was crying, "Goodnight! Come again."

He went on toward the house, intending to get his car keys so he could put the Chevrolet in the garage, but he had not even reached the porch steps when he heard the taxi stop at the foot of the drive and the horn sound.

He looked around. The window beside Lily Loyd was rolling slowly downward.

"Mr. Komar?" came the old, weak voice.

He set down the chair and hurried across the lawn to her.

"Yes, Mrs. Loyd?"

"You'll come to see me, won't you, before you go?"

"I'll come Friday night," he said.

"I was wrong, you know," she went on.

He waited, not knowing to what she referred. After all, he thought himself that she was wrong about many things.

"This is the south side, isn't it?" she asked, when he was silent.

"Yes," he acknowledged.

"Do you remember what I said once—it seems a long time ago—about . . ."

"I remember," he answered. He did. Her casual remark, that first evening, about "factories and foreigners" had, if he had known it, struck the note that was later to sound louder and louder in all their ears, leading finally—for had it not?—to their present situation.

"I remember," he repeated.

"That visit happened years ago," she said. "I was younger, younger and tougher. It seemed tonight—" She broke off. "But then," she went on, almost shyly, "you are my friend, aren't you?"

He replied gently, "I am your friend."

"That is what *really* makes the difference, isn't it?" she asked.

"All the difference," he promised her.

"Why," she presently exclaimed, "I think we may win!"

"I hope so."

"You and I." She wished her meaning clear.

"*For* Blanche," he interpreted.

"That's it. Just so. Then . . ."

"Goodnight," he said.

"Friday?"

"On Friday."

"Goodnight," she called. "Goodnight!"

The cab backed into the street, straightened itself out, and almost at once was lost to sight beyond the straight-marching light poles. He turned and went slowly into the house.

• 19 •

ALL Friday afternoon wet snow fell and melted and continued to fall and melt. But toward the quick end of daylight, toward five on that falling winter day, the air, too, quickened, and the snowflakes, from formless blobs, became hard and discernible particularities. The air rustled with their steady, relentless presence, and the streets drifted half an inch deep in what looked like crystal in the headlights of cars, or were abruptly exposed in fan-shaped patches by the intermittent wind.

Mr. Komar stayed late at his office, late and alone in the long room with its series of depending electric lights and its battery of olive-green files that made a passageway to the glass-walled executive offices. The interior lights cast their sheen on the office windows: the night and the rising storm were invisible. But as he sorted papers, wrote a series of memoranda, straightened his desk (and even dusted it), he felt the so substantial interior reverberate: the window sashes rattled; inexplicably, one of the ceiling globes set up a slow revolution on its chain; and in the outer hallway the wheeze of the night elevator sounded like an expiring whisper from the alone building. The office was a dead place, more vacant than the empty nighttime room of any house, for here were no affections to leave their residue of memory and assurance: here was the graveyard of L.C. Smith and Royal, of Grand Rapids oak and metal posture chairs, of linoleum runners, filing baskets, spindles, and leather books of unhumane figures. This was the place where affection could not get in, and this the place where utility perpetually threatened to collapse for lack of it.

Mr. Komar made his parting arrangements with the heady sensation that he would never come back. He knew, of course, that he would, on next Wednesday morning at the latest, and to document his conviction he made a note to himself of a matter to be acted on that day. But in the same manner that the storm, tidelike, swept against the dead center of the office and receded, an emotion quite of an extraordinary excitement would engulf him and then spill away, leaving him hollow and weak, and more assured than ever that this was somehow a final departure. The dream was coming true: he would see the house, the happy rural seat. When the wave broke across him he had to put aside his books, and even as it receded he had to wait to finish his memorandum, for his hand trembled with the expectation that the emotion promised to fulfill. He dreamed of Mary Bush, and he knew that at the happy rural seat he would possess her. He had the dreamer's confidence, and his imperviousness to time and to difficulty. Standing in the long wooden house on the bleak rise of ground, he would lift his arms and across the years, across the momentous century, Mary Bush would reach out to him. He would love her and he would be free. The moment could not possibly be tarnished; not even this metallic office could intimidate it. He would spring up fresh and shining in the instant of their communion, whole, solid, sure, a living man in a time not surely so isolated as those descendants of Mary Bush made it out to be. He would love because he expected to find out what love was. There would be no fumbling, no talk, only the intense and shining silence. He would know what to do. What to do? About —"everything," he thought. He would penetrate to the truth that his vision of Mary Bush indicated: the truth that framed the beautiful woman in the cracked portrait, the blank-faced invalid in the group photograph, the seamstress pricking her finger and spilling blood on the patchwork quilt;—the truth that had sometime, like a river, run underground and needed to be dug up, brought to the surface again: the truth that would give justification to Lily Loyd and life to her daughter Blanche. And Blanche? With a dreamer's practicality he had placed her, bowed and submissive, on a hearth in the farmhouse room, and as Mary Bush laid her hands on him, so would he lay his hands on Blanche. They would be finished with the rural seat forever. Whatever it meant to Blanche and her mother—whether that real identity which they believed only a fixed place gives; whether that sense of form and beauty and hierarchy they had only known as something lost to them—whatever this currency of selfhood was at this moment suspended in time, it would be transmuted at the rural seat to the only positive wealth that he had come to understand, in these last weeks, there was: the wealth of love.

Then, was it right to feel that he would never come back to this hollow office? It was right, he thought; it was right. For it was the man that the looking glass saw who wrote these notes, stored this duster back in its bottom drawer; the man shut off. He could not last long. The hard glass bulged. The pale beast would die.

When he put out the lights and shut the office door behind him, it was with as firm a sense of parting as he had ever experienced in his life. He went down the hall almost jauntily: the image was for all the world that of winning a jackpot on Bank Night at the theater; he saw himself going down the long, sloping aisle, past the rows of spectators, and climbing up onto the lighted stage: signaled out and advancing gloriously alone, he received the prize. For he did believe that the empty years, the years as a trapped and insignificant spectator, were presently, and quite soon, to be done with. He was mounting into some extraordinary and divine light. As he rang for the elevator, he remembered how, on that Monday night that had witnessed his first visit in Grant

Street, his own little, insignificant spotlight had wheeled up from the dark sidewalk and wonderfully merged itself in the brilliance of a street light. His mind had run on at the time—engaged as it had been in the particulars of meeting Miss Loyd, of merely conducting himself, though even then he had had his dream of lighted porches and shining houses, and dancers skipping across driveways. During that evening, and again and again in the days that followed, he had witnessed other occasions of light: his glance meeting Blanche Loyd's in a sustained tension on the porch in Grant Street; the brilliant, sunny day in the country, which for all its subsequent disaster had done much to get things, as he so ardently desired them to be, "clear." And he wondered, even, if there were not some quite consistent meaning in the fact that in the early days at the Loyds' house he had been obliged to grope toward their dark meanings in rooms that were so often themselves dark, opaque, hard to discern. The climax and the change had come in total darkness, as he knelt beside Lily Loyd's tapestry chair, with only the glow of the gas fireplace to point the black, and was that not somehow appropriate? He thought it was. Now they were all approaching dawn, he told himself as he pushed through the revolving door onto the snowy street.

He ate hurriedly in a counter restaurant in the next block, near the lot where the Chevrolet was parked. Even so, it was after eight when he gave his ticket to the attendant and waded through the snow to the car. The Chevrolet started at once; he had left it all day Thursday at the garage, as he always did before he set off on any kind of journey, and it was exuberant with oil, alcohol, and sparkplugs. He drove carefully along the slippery, empty thoroughfares that led to the west side. The car slithered up the bridge over the industrial valley, and he seemed to soar through waste heights of cold and snow. The valley beneath him was invisible. When he came down into the streets on the farther side of the bridge, it was like the descent into a city of ice, as if the square and rigid buildings were hard blocks carved out of a monumental cliff. The lights in the windows of houses and stores and apartments looked brilliant, but subterranean; the streets were empty both of pedestrians and automobiles; only once he passed a bus that roared like some fuzzy monster through the glacial corridors in a ritual that had lost its meaning, for there were no passengers. The interior people, Mr. Komar thought, had retreated deep into their caves of ice. He traveled between their glassy walls, an alien and happy creature, feeling himself gloriously dispossessed.

Grant Street, in its glittering shroud, looked splendid and fantastic to him as he turned off Kingery and made his way toward the Loyds'. The common properties of the long wooden façade on either side—the uniform front porches and doorways and number of windows—merged into an obscurity that seemed to accede to the demands of the night and his imagination for the extraordinary. He advanced, as he radiantly saw it, between improbable towers and bristling, glassy bays, beneath ornate and frosty cupolas, past fences of lacy iron over which peered stags frozen forever immobile in marble squares; his way was lighted, it seemed, by row on row of chandeliers suspended from ebony trees. He knew he went forward toward a throne, and that he would receive there from the queen a glove, or a word, or a kiss that he must carry with him on the beautiful quest.

He was therefore not really surprised to see the Loyd house lighted up as he had never seen it before. Lamps blazed in every room, upstairs as well as down. The snow on the front walk was scuffled as if by the passage of many feet, and as he locked the car and turned to the house the front door flew open, and the storm door was pushed outward.

Mrs. Mentone looked toward him through the falling snow, but she was apparently blinded by the porch light, for she did not call any greeting. As he climbed the steps he saw the expression on her face alter: from expectation it collapsed into anxiety.

"I thought it was the doctor," she said as he came up.

"The doctor?"

"He should be back by now. He went to pick up a nurse."

They went into the house and shut the door without any of their customary formality, and he was already slipping out of his coat as he asked, "She's ill?"

The housekeeper took his coat from him automatically, without replying, and carried it over to the hat rack and put it down.

"Is she ill?" he repeated.

"Yes."

That was all she was able at once to bring out. When she turned back to him he saw that her face, under the overhead light, was haggard, and that her eyes were an ugly red.

"I don't know why I took your coat," she went on, touching it with her fingertips. "I think you'd better go."

She bent over to pick up the coat once more, but he crossed to her quickly and caught her arm.

"Is it serious?"

Again, it was a moment before she replied. "I've wired Blanche," she said. She began to cry.

He patted her arm gingerly, and after a moment her crying broke off. "When?" he asked.

"I sent the wire this morning. She should be here in an hour or so. Lou's gone to meet her."

"I didn't know," he explained apologetically.

"No, it's my fault. I forgot you were coming tonight."

"I suppose . . . Is she conscious?"

"She was, a few minutes ago."

"Does the doctor—"

"I don't know! I don't know!" She started to cry again. "Will you *please* take your coat?"

"But, what happened?"

"It was the trip Wednesday night," said Mrs. Mentone angrily; "that stupid trip. She's been in bed ever since." She turned on him, furious. "Why didn't you keep out of it when I asked you to? We were all right."

"I knew nothing about the trip," he protested.

"But you kept hammering away at her; that's why she did it."

"I couldn't have stopped her," he pointed out, reasonably.

She wiped her eyes. "No, nothing could have stopped her. It got too big." She sighed and rubbed her nose. "Don't think . . . Don't mind what I say."

"You were angry with me Wednesday night, weren't you?"

"Angry!" she said fiercely. "I could have killed you. I knew then what was coming." She paused and looked at him with the red light of fear in her eyes. "That night I saw the ball."

"You *saw* it!" he echoed, shocked.

She nodded at the closed door between the living room and the hall. "In there. I put her to bed and came back a few minutes later with her medicine. She was asleep, and the ball was . . . crouched down beside her on the quilt. It"–she shuddered–"it didn't even know I was there."

He took her arm firmly, but she pulled away and faced him, stricken.

"I tell you it was there! And I know . . . I knew finally what it meant. It doesn't come for me! There's its evil. It takes what you love, what you depend on." She began to sob. "What will become of *us?*" she whimpered. "Yes, that's what it means. It comes and leaves you–nothing."

"Nothing!" he whispered, horrified.

"Nothing, nothing . . ." she crooned.

His horror made him cruel, and desperately he strove to break the spell she had flung around both of them. He looked at her grimly. "You'll get your wish: you and your husband can go away."

"Oh, God!" she whispered. "Where? To *nothing* . . ."

"But I," he went on wonderingly, and the spell was shattered before this further revelation, "I'll never be able to go–now."

She understood him, and in her large eyes there was a certain triumph, a paying back to him for the disaster he had brought on the house. "She'll be home tonight."

"I'll never see it," he said, and he thought he could hardly bear the terrible grief, the rude ending of his dream. "I'll never know how it meant so much to them. I'll never see Mary Bush!"

"No," she agreed, "it ends tonight."

"Let me see her," he demanded. "I won't believe it! I won't believe that it can end this way. She'll know what to do; she couldn't *rest* knowing how things are with us."

"*She* won't care!" cried Annabelle Mentone. "She'll be home tonight, too." She sat down on the hat rack and began, horribly, to laugh. She brought her rough, garishly lacquered hands up and covered her face, and presently he saw tears running out between her fingers.

He said, taking her arms and drawing her hands away from the mottled face, "I'll fight your ball. . . ."

She drew in a deep breath. "There's nothing to fight," she answered bitterly.

He leaned forward and lightly kissed the powdered, lined forehead. "She'll be waiting for me," he said. "She'll have heard us."

"I'll have to come with you."

"No." It was not a command, nor even a request. It was a statement of unalterable fact, and she took it as such.

"I'll be in the kitchen. But you mustn't stay long. She wants . . . You won't tire her? I know she wants to see Blanche."

He caught one of her hands and squeezed it, but "My poor Lily" was the answer he made. Alone and for the last time he went through the large kitchen, through the cluttered dining room, into the living room of that house that was so unlike and so far removed from the happy rural seat.

He was prepared for the figure in the old brass bed, but he was not prepared for the shock of the empty tapestry chair, with its frayed arms and its lace doilies that were so pitiably and forever in place. He almost cried when he looked at those doilies, and at the blanket that lay neatly folded on the seat of the chair. He lifted his eyes to the portrait of Mary Bush. Her blue eyes held their secret. She gazed away from him, withdrawn from him in her century's dust and memories, at the photograph on the mantel.

"Mary Bush," he whispered. "*Mary Bush!*" he begged.

"Herbert." Lily Loyd's voice was surprisingly strong; he thought, as he went quickly to the bed, that it carried the last strength of her mortality.

He knelt and took one of her hands strongly in his own. "I was up to my old trick," he said in a firm voice. "I was riddling Mary Bush, but she slips away from me as she always has. Tonight, though"—he thought of the splendor of his dream—"tonight I felt as if I'd really learn the truth—somehow, when I got over to her, over there."

"Well, I am here," said Lily Loyd.

"The old curmudgeon," he answered.

She tried to lift her head, but she was too weak. She squeezed his hand faintly. "Those were my words for *her*," she answered. "Is this the time to make fun of me?"

"I'd *never* . . ." His voice broke.

She was silent for a time.

"I don't believe I'll see Blanche," she said.

"Why, she'll be here inside the hour. Of course you will!"

She grunted. "I'm sorry to see your honesty go."

"Then don't back me into corners," he retorted.

She smiled. "That's better. What's it doing out?"

"There's a storm, but it's—splendid. I wish I could tell you what I felt tonight, knowing I was coming to you. I came from another world, a world all frozen. I came into—ours."

"Ours?"

"Yours and mine. The one we've made—or can make, now, somehow."

"I'll make no world," she said sadly.

"But I shall—for you," he answered. "Is it so lastingly important, something like this? Won't you trust *me* to carry it on?"

She turned her head away on the pillow. Her breathing was so shallow that there was no motion at all to the covers. After she had been quiet for what seemed to him a dangerous interval, he leaned closer to the bed. "Lily!" he said. When she did not answer, a stab of pain and grief went through him. "Lily?" he called.

"I was thinking of what you said," she replied; and then she went on gruffly, "You are very casual about my fate."

In his relief he laughed out. "Oh, Lily!" he answered.

"It is strange," she said, "that I should wait—wait like this with a man I've known—how long? How long is it?"

"Forever," he assured her. "And always—always." He took a deep breath. "I'll man the ship!" he again promised her.

"No," she objected, "don't do that. The ship is putting into port. You were right when you said it would never carry another cargo. I want—something for Blanche, for you, bigger and more beautiful. I want—the happiness of the rural seat for you."

"But that's . . ." he began.

"That is not what you just promised me," she countered. "Dear friend," she went on, "don't mix up the real thing with one embodiment of it, as I have done all these years—all of my life," she concluded sadly.

"You want the happiness for us?" he asked.

"Yes. I've thought often, here in my darkness, of what was said Wednesday night, in particular of how those women seemed a chattering, vulgar echo of Blanche and myself. I felt ashamed. I feel ashamed now. I have been stupid, Herbert: it is the inevitable sin of a proud people. I saw that night how we'd all spent ourselves on the dead issue. It was my fault, my doing. I have mourned an institution. Worse than that, I have mourned a fiction self-constructed out of my failure. When I said to you—when was it? was it as we left?—that the real distinction was friendship, was love, I wanted to show you my vision."

"Your vision?"

"This house,"—he saw her lids flicker open, and he knew that in memory her eyes ranged across the room, through the partitions into the rooms beyond and above;—"I tried to believe in it as a continuation of the rural seat, to redeem the betrayal I made forty years ago. I thought that betrayal lay in selling a house; I thought if we could only make things again what they had been. . . ." Her thin lips curved in a smile, and in her next words he caught the ironic repetition of what Mrs. Hlavaty had said to him Wednesday night. "I, too, have sinned against you, Herbert." The quick humor expired; he felt her hand struggle in his, clench itself. "How could I help it, since I had long before that sinned against myself? I have lived all these years in a mortal fear. Once, as I told you, I believed that men were born for great ends." Her voice died away in fatigue.

"You've kept your faith as best you could in these days."

She frowned, and something of her old vigor flared in her voice. "These days, these days! As if our faith had anything to do with the time we live in: our faith should let us rise above any time, *any* place! You sound too much like myself when you say that. I," she brought out with a terrible humility, "have kept no faith except anger." He was about to protest, but as if expecting this she squeezed his hand feebly, and he remained silent. "And you, Herbert," she said gently, turning her head toward him, "you'll never see our rural seat."

He put his forehead down on their locked hands, and presently he heard her free hand brush across the quilt and felt it touch his hair.

"That's why," she said, "I want to try to show it to you: to show you how a good life went bad in our cautious keeping." He heard her draw her breath laboriously in. "Bits and pieces," she went on, "that's all I can give you any more. We weren't rich or great back there, you know—not one of the grand families. Oh, yes! we had them. There was the beauty of that place, if you like: we were for a time all life in a lovely miniature." She was silent again; then, she chuckled. "The mean pleasure I used to get when our people visited us over here! The vengeance I had in exacting from them an admiration of our bathroom, of our electric lights!

I had attached myself to plumbing and light bulbs as once I had been attached in a thoughtless innocence to all the large beauties of life—all the things we did and believed in over there, without really knowing why we thought as we did or acted as we acted." Her crooked fingers moved slowly across his hair. "You can measure the change in me from this: that I hung up the portrait of Mary Bush when we came to this house; Mary Bush whom—let me say it at last—I always hated."

"Why did you hate her?"

She was silent a long time. "I think," she said finally, "because she knew how things really were."

He lifted his head. "She was an outsider, like me; and a foreigner. Perhaps that's what started it. But you really hated her because she loved."

"Yes," agreed Lily Loyd, "she loved, and she knew what it was that she loved. We couldn't forgive her for knowing what we were ignorant of."

"Tell me," he urged, "what it was she knew."

"I'll tell you what I know now," answered Lily Loyd. "That is as close as we shall ever come to Mary Bush." She turned her head away. "Bits and pieces," she murmured sadly.

"Give them to me!" he commanded. "I love, too. I'll love them into a whole."

"I will talk about myself." She chuckled almost soundlessly. "The ego's last gasp? No matter. Lily Armstrong: how worn away now is the girl who bore that name—yet, I am she. 'The invincible Lily,' Mary called me. I never quite knew how she meant it. We were nearly of an age, and I resented what I took as her show of greater experience. Perhaps, if I had only asked her once . . . but I didn't. I always answered her one way. 'Well, so I am!' I'd say. 'I am invincible.' And Mary smiled, and I was angry. Lily Armstrong: I thought that pretty, contented Lily was indestructible, for she bore within her the past, a past full of Armstrongs as far back as, it seemed, the Ontario country went. We had been in Yarmouth and Southwold so long, just as the Loyds had been, and other families, Johnsons, Haydens, Blacks, MacMillans. . . ."

Her voice sank into a whisper, and then into silence as, Mr. Komar thought, in memory she told again the innumerable names of those old, those invincible families.

Presently, she said, "And what a clutter of relations!—cousins, half-cousins, great-aunts, grandparents. . . . There was no need to force one's way through to what one was: perhaps there is where the early danger lay. I cannot ever remember at that time questioning or marveling at the reality of being myself. The past was a living forest at the backs of all of us who were young: we were its . . . what will I call us?—its saplings. And oh! the lovely assurance of knowing that in time we would grow tall and dense, too, and that the forest would go on reaching out. From the day I grew old enough to understand my role in that society, I knew that I would marry one of the Johnson boys, or one of the Loyds at the old house on the ridge, or one of my distant Armstrong connections. It was never imagined—certainly least of all by me—that I'd marry above myself—or below. The distinctions among us were sanctioned by the past, and because they seemed to everyone that I knew right and natural, there were—though you will think me blind from sentiment as well as cataracts—there were few harsh divisions among us. If a man moved up in the scale, we applauded him"—she laughed—"after a generation or two; and if he slipped down, we overlooked it—for a generation or two." She commented, querulously, "But I don't make things clear!"

"Don't stop," he said.

"Then, what do I remember? . . . I remember how we talked! I used to be quite hoarse by the time spring came and the year opened out again. I think . . ." She paused, uncertain. "I think we were attached to a great many ideals, to charity, friendship, even, a little—though it is a curious thing to say of the human creature—even to humility. We did work hard, all of us, but there was time for using what our hands had made, too, what our hearts had long ago told us was right for men to make and do. We could not travel far, but we traveled . . . we traveled widely," she brought out exultantly, "in the whole republic of our hearts." Once again she broke off. "I am too tired," she said sadly. "I can only make pictures for you, and tell you the stories we endlessly told each other. I remember the story of the rural seat, how there was gold enough hidden in its walls to make us rich for life. That first Loyd who rafted up the St. Lawrence from a settlement in the colonies had brought gold with him in little kegs. Some of the kegs were lost in a storm on the river, and when he built the rural seat he hid the rest of them. The beauty of our way of life, I would try to make you understand, is that during the great age he lived to he never had occasion to unearth his fortune. He died with his secret. The gold is no legend, I promise you that. If there is not so much as we talked of, still there is somewhere in that house some of it. The beauty is that though we talked about it, we of the later generations, though we dreamed of finding it and seeing . . . seeing the *world*," she said contemptuously, "only the children ever hunted for it. The rest of us knew that we already had the world, and time enough to live it in."

"Yet," Mr. Komar said, "something went wrong."

"Something went wrong," agreed Lily Loyd. "Something . . . what time is it?"

He started to turn round to look at the mantel clock, but suddenly she caught at him with a desperate strength. "No, don't tell me. No one should know the hour he dies at." As her grip on him slipped off, she said, "After all, Herbert, I am a little afraid. I think this is when I used . . . used to have my coffee. Would you like Annabelle to bring you some coffee?"

"I—" But he could not go on.

She said, slowly, "No, I know what you would say. There is no time. But it would be pleasant, wouldn't it, this once more?" She impatiently wiped her eye. "I'm an old fool! What a time to get sentimental. Time! time!" she exclaimed. "The minutes go on: this is my last chance to rise above them. But I am afraid to start right in again; I am afraid they will go by too fast. What does the room look like now?"

"This room? It looks fine."

"There's a light on?"

"The one by your chair."

"And my blanket? Did she leave my blanket there?"

"Yes."

"You never know. I might . . . I might want it. How do you look tonight? What have you got on?"

"It's an old suit, brown."

"Oh, so much," she said, "so much about you I would have liked to know! I'm glad you've got your hair. I never could abide a bald-headed man. Do you look after your clothes?"

"I try to."

"And Mrs. Hlavaty—I said it right, did I?—she treats you well enough now? I was sorry. I heard, you know, about your troubles."

"She's fine. Everything's fine."

"Would you tell Annabelle that I . . . that I never had so much fun until she came?"

"I'll tell her."

"Then . . . well, I'll go on again. Have you ever seen a snow-storm globe?"

"You have one in the parlor."

"Yes, I'd forgotten. That's what we were like. The years of peace had made us cautious, and we were poised, beautiful and still intact, on a crumbling base. When Mary came, the year after Jerry and I were married, she was the crack in the glass. I am tempted to put too much weight on her coming. Of course she was only the dog we whipped because all around us the wolves were yelping on the walls."

The clock began to ring.

"Oh, cover my ears!" she cried. "I don't want to know what time it is!"

He put his hands across her ears, and her voice went on, lifting and falling above the inexorable statement of the clock. When it had stopped they were both exhausted. He could feel cold perspiration running down the insides of his arms, and Lily Loyd's hands were like ice.

She began to speak more quickly, and he leaned forward to hear her. "Somewhere, she had seen the ragged world, and she made us know how our own world had sunk down around us. Down and down. . . ." Her mind seemed to wander. She asked sharply, "Why do you want my house?"

He kept tight hold on her hand. "For Blanche," he said clearly. "For Blanche and me."

She was still, her eyelids shut. He settled himself more comfortably, and finally she came back to him.

"Herbert?"

"I am here."

"I believe I was having a little nap. You were so long."

"Sixty years too late," he said, "but not *too* late."

"Sixty years . . . and when you came you marked the beginning of the end, just as her coming did—Mary's. But I'll not fight it this time."

"This time you've won," he told her.

"How you rock my composure!" she said. "She was a good sort, for one of her class. I must do her justice now, mustn't I?"

"Mary Bush?"

"Yes, Mary. . . . She came in the fall—the loveliest day. The poplars down the drive were all yellow, like coins, I remember, as if they'd tapped the gold in the house. My husband brought her and Jeremiah up from town in the spring wagon. She was the littlest thing, more like a child than a woman, until you saw her eyes, and the line of her jaw. They told you. She had on a sprigged blue and white dress, and I thought she must be the McKendrick girl from down toward Long Point, who was coming to spend a month with us. You see, we'd heard nothing of my father-in-law since he left, except to tell us when to meet him. But when he swung Mary down out of the wagon I knew . . . I knew that wasn't Thursa McKendrick. He brought her over to me, and he said, 'Lily, this is Mary,' and I looked at her, and I was afraid. There was something about her even then, the look in her face. I didn't think anybody had a right to look as happy as that. I was afraid. Now it seems to me a cloud went over the sun right then, right there when she put out her hand to me, but I don't think it did. I said, 'Jeremiah Loyd, you're a *fool!*' . . . and I was wrong. She loved him. Then I turned and marched into the house. And I looked at it and hated it—*her* house. But," she sighed, "we settled down, she and I did, and when her baby miscarried I was the one who brought her back. That'd happened to me, twice. I knew. I knew. The picture was made soon after. She never had another child. And, in coming among us, as I thought, too soon, she'd come too late. We had eaten the bitter fruit of the jealous self long, long before, and we loved no one because we did not love ourselves." She moved her body slowly, on the pillows. "She had the darkest blue eyes! If I can push myself up, will you put another pillow under me?"

He got up and gently raised her.

"In the spring," she said, "there's wild mustard all over the hillside, and the tombstones so old that some of the names are gone from them. My husband was the eldest son, and after they took Mary up there the house came to us. Then Jerry died so soon, and I sold it. There was no reason to keep it on, I thought. I sold it gladly, angrily. I wanted my children to have a bigger chance than their father had had to"—she grunted—"to 'get on' in life. I came here. My sons escaped me, though I cannot think the scattered life they've made has altogether justified their rebellion. And Blanche—all her life I've watched her, cautioned her. I spoiled Blanche for love because I was afraid love would pull this house down around us. And it's right," she said, "it's right that those stones should fade, for it's life that matters, and even now I scorn a benign hereafter."

Her hand lay very still in his, and then it began to jerk convulsively; he saw that every breath had become a separate battle for her, and that, in truth, her expiation was her death. He got stiffly to his feet and sat down on the crocheted cover of the Chair, and perhaps five minutes went by in which they did not speak.

"I believe in that way of life," Lily Loyd said finally, "though it is gone forever. What we have now is no substitute, it is a calamity. But we can go on; we aren't lost. Who said it? Who said, 'Life *is* communicable'? Ah!" she cried in a strangled voice, "love her, Herbert!"

He came swiftly to her side. "I will! I will!" he promised.

"Tell her," she said, in a voice that was scarcely audible, "what you can about tonight—about the life we're making here."

"I love her," was all he said.

"Then you'll fight," she whispered, satisfied. She made a last joke. "You'll do as they did over there, long ago, conquer the virgin territory!"

They began to laugh. He leaned over and kissed her soft, dry cheek, and he saw his tears dropping on her skin.

"Mary Bush!" he cried jubilantly. He caught her in his arms.

"Dear friend!" she said, and she died.